HEROES OF GOD SERIES

HEROES OF GOD SERIES

This is a book in the HEROES OF GOD series.

Other books in the series include:

The series will include books about Luke, Elijah, John the Apostle, Martin Luther, Francis of Assisi, John Mark, and other biblical, historical, and modern church pioneers of our religious heritage.

The HEROES OF GOD series is under the general editorship of Albert N. Williams and Ann West Williams.

JOHN THE BAPTIST
PROPHET OF CHRIST

JOHN THE BAPTIST

From a painting by Hans Baldung

HEROES OF GOD SERIES

John the Baptist
Prophet of Christ

by

SLATER BROWN

ASSOCIATION PRESS

NEW YORK

JOHN THE BAPTIST, PROPHET OF CHRIST

Copyright, 1955, by Slater Brown

FIRST PRINTING

Library of Congress catalog card number: 55-7409

 55

Printed in the United States of America
American Book–Stratford Press, Inc., New York

CONTENTS

1. THE ASSASSINS

EVEN FROM A DISTANCE Asher hadn't liked the looks of
the two pilgrims. Herding his sheep into the fold for the
night, he had noticed the two coming along the road.
Though they carried staffs in their hands and wore the
white robes of Essenes, they did not walk like ordinary
pilgrims, footsore and weary after a long day's journey.
Their step was sure, their gait like that of a pair of
gladiators striding across the bloodstained sands of an
arena.

At the foot of the hill the pair halted and called to
Asher. Picking up the club he used to protect his flock
from the wolves that infested that region of Palestine
east of the river Jordan, he sauntered down to ask what
they wanted.

"We are two humble Essenes, two pilgrims," they told
him, "on our way to hear the new prophet. Good shepherd, does this road lead straight on to Bethabara?"

Before answering, Asher looked the men over. One
was a man of middle age, with a hooked nose, a lean

face, and shrewd eyes. The other was young, with a heavy, brooding mouth, enormous hands, and the eyes of a jackal. Asher briefly told them the way—straight south along the river Jordan, with a sharp turn to the right at the ruined tower. "It's hardly a dozen miles," he said.

The older of the two glanced toward the setting sun. "Too late, then, to get there before night," he grumbled. "Any town nearby?"

Asher shook his head. On this side of the Jordan, he told them, Bethabara itself was the nearest village.

Mumbling a blessing that sounded suspiciously like a curse, the two turned to go, but at that moment a gust of wind caught the younger man's robe and flipped it open. He hastily seized it and gathered the folds back in place, but not quickly enough to prevent Asher from detecting the flash of naked steel.

"A filthy wind!" the young man muttered, scowling, as he joined his companion.

Club in hand, Asher stood in the road, happy to see the pair move on. If he had not liked their looks when he had first seen them, he liked them even less now. It wasn't only the sight of the weapon that had increased his suspicions. In that hilly country with its prowling wolves and its bandits, there was every reason for a traveler to carry side arms. And sometimes it was wiser to carry them hidden. But Asher knew that it was unusual for an Essene to carry weapons of any kind, for that strange sect, living in isolated colonies along the shores of the Dead Sea, were peaceful folk who held it a sin even to manufacture a steel weapon.

As they reached the bend in the road, one of the men halted and stared back at Asher. Then, spitting into the dust, he went on. A moment later they had disappeared around the turn.

Asher was well satisfied to see the two white robes pass out of sight. With a sigh of relief he climbed the hill back to his flock. But he had hardly begun herding his sheep together when, glancing up, he saw a thin column of smoke rising from behind the wind-blasted growth of cedars near the broken tower. He stopped and stared at it.

"They've halted and pitched camp," he thought as he gazed with worried eyes at the rising smoke. "What are they? A couple of sheep thieves?"

Though it seemed unlikely that the pair had come to steal his sheep, Asher decided to investigate. Leaning his shepherd's staff against a rock, he picked up his club again and started off toward the telltale column of smoke. He skirted the hill, crept through the grove of stunted cedars, and then, dropping on his hands and knees, crawled toward the fire, where, he assumed, the two strangers would be cooking their supper. A thick bush of thorns stood between him and the fire. Asher crept toward it. Gently parting the thorny branches with his club, he peered at the two men.

They were, as Asher had expected, squatting before the fire, their white robes pulled up over their knees and an open sack of provisions lying between them. Each held a dagger, using it as a skewer to broil chunks of meat over the glowing coals. The tempting smell drifted toward Asher, but though it made his mouth water, it also redoubled his suspicions. For he knew that—even granting that Essenes might on occasion carry arms—the strict rules of the order forbade them to eat flesh. Moreover, unaware that they were being watched, the men had dropped all pretense of being humble pilgrims. As they sat grimly broiling their meat, they looked even less like pilgrims who would trudge many weary miles to hear the inspired words of a prophet.

For several moments the two silently watched their meat sputtering over the coals. Finally the younger of the two spoke.

"How are we to tell him from the others," he asked, "this John the Dipper?"

The older man did not answer at once. Thoughtfully, he turned his meat over the coals. "Another stupid question," he remarked. "John the Baptist doesn't dress like his followers. He's easily recognized by his mangy camel's-hair coat and his leather girdle."

"A half-starved fanatic, I take it, and easy to handle."

The older man glanced sideways at his companion. "Don't fool yourself, fellow. He's not one of your palace fops. They tell me he's a big man, strong as a bull, not much older than you are, and afraid of nothing. You've got a young lion on your hands and don't think you haven't."

The young man tipped up his dagger and inspected his meat. "Haven't botched a job yet," he muttered.

"Leave it to me. Before I was ten a Phoenician sailor had taught me all there is to know about handling a knife—every devilish Phoenician trick there is."

The older man lapsed into silence again. Asher, peering through the bush, watched him as he drew his broiled meat from the fire, sniffed it, and then deftly rolled it in a leathery slab of bread.

"Keep your Phoenician tricks to yourself," he growled as he bit off a hunk, "until I say the word. For the time being you and I are a pair of half-witted disciples of this John the Baptist. You won't find the role difficult, I imagine."

"At your orders, Captain!" the young man remarked, making a face. "But the whole business is a mystery to me."

"Forget the mystery," said the older man. "Just try to get through that thick skull of yours these two points. The first is that you don't get paid until the job's done. The second is that King Herod's own spies mustn't suspect us."

"You let the cat out of the bag that time!" the young man grinned.

"What?" the older man asked, looking bored. "What did I let slip?"

"That we're not agents of King Herod."

"Who said we were?"

The younger man shrugged his shoulders. "I took it for granted." He thought a moment, then turned to the older man. "So that was the queen, then, Queen Herodias herself, who came in with the chamberlain?"

The captain poked the fire with the blade of his dagger. "Did she look like a queen?" he asked.

"My idea of one. By the gods, I've never seen bigger jewels on whiter hands! Or such bracelets!"

"Made your eyes pop, eh?"

"And her perfume. The first time in my life I'd ever got a real whiff of spikenard—it filled the whole palace room! I'm still dizzy with it. I only wish, though, that she'd unveiled her face, just for a moment." A dreamy expression came into the young man's eyes. "You can hardly blame old Herod for stealing that Jezebel away from his brother. I'd have done the same thing myself." He paused a moment. "But what puzzles me now is why a queen like her should have it in for this flea-bitten prophet."

The older man poked the fire again. "Never ask the reasons for a woman's hatred," he said. "You might get scorched by it yourself. Forget the reason. It's her secret."

"But you say that Herod has spies watching the Dipper, too. What reason has *he* got?"

"In his case it's no secret. As you remarked, John is a prophet. You ought to know that always spells trouble for any ruler. Don't you know your own Jewish history?"

"I've told you before, I'm not a Jew." The young man's voice grew shrill. "I'm a Roman citizen, born in Tarsus."

"Of Jewish parents. Your speech betrays you." The older man stopped suddenly and looked up. "Quiet!" he whispered. "What's that sound?"

Asher had been so intent on overhearing every word

the two strangers uttered that he had not noticed the sound himself. But now, in the abrupt silence and far behind him, he heard the distant tinkle of a bell.

It was only the slightest sound, gentle and ever so far away. Yet it clanged in Asher's ears like a gong. For he realized that coming toward him across the hills, following his trail with a blind instinct that knew no danger, bleating a petulant complaint at having been left behind, trotted his little goat.

Asher's hand tightened on his club. He knew the goat would find him and betray his position. He hardly dared shift his glance. The two men, staring in his direction, might even detect the movement of his eyes. He lay breathless as he saw the older man rise and, shading his eyes, peer toward the hill from where the sound came.

Asher watched him. He saw the man's face relax. "A goat," he said, and squatted down by the fire again. "A goat straying from the flock back there." He took a bite of food and chewed thoughtfully for a moment. "You Jews are a queer race of men," he observed.

"I've already told you," the younger man protested, "that I . . ."

"Forget it," the older man cut in. "A strange race troubled by strange beliefs. You think you're a chosen people, a special order of human beings set apart from the rest of us. You believe a Messiah is coming who'll set up a new kingdom."

"And that's what worries Herod?"

"Exactly. He and his generals fear an uprising."

"But the queen! Why does she have it in for this John the Dipper? Why . . . ?"

Asher did not hear the older man's answer to the question. He could only hear the bell now, growing louder every instant. There was a break in the sound, as if the animal had halted to crop a few leaves on her way. But she was soon trotting along again, so close now that Asher could hear her gentle bleating and the sound of her hoofs. Lying there, he realized that in a moment the gentle bleating would rise to a cry of recognition as the goat caught sight of him.

There was no time to lose. He knew he must get out before the goat betrayed his presence. He must get up and run. But first he had to get out of range of a knife, two knives perhaps, streaking through the twilight toward his back. Slowly he released the thorny branch he had pushed aside and carefully began working his way backward. In front of him he could hear the voices of the two men, behind him the insistent tinkle of the bell.

A twig snapped beneath the weight of his body. He heard the men's voices abruptly halt, and he lay there, flattening himself upon the rocky ground. He tried to repeat a prayer, but couldn't remember one.

The little goat was now hardly a hundred paces behind him. Suddenly the sound of the bell and the bleating ceased. And, breaking the silence, Asher now heard a different sound.

At any other time the sound would have meant danger to him. At any other time it would have put him instantly on guard. But now, as Asher heard it echoing across the hills, he knew that, though his little goat might be doomed, his own life had perhaps been spared. For the sound he heard, bloodcurdling to any shepherd but now like the voice of providence, was the howl and yelp of a pair of hunting wolves.

At the first yelp the tinkling bell had gone mute. Asher knew that the goat had stopped dead in her tracks. He pictured her standing there in the darkness, with her long, drooping ears, her delicate head raised. He knew that in a moment she would whirl around and, scampering over the rocky hill, make for protection among his sheep.

"What's that now?" Asher heard one of the men exclaim.

"A pair of wolves hunting their supper." This was the older man speaking. "Toss on more wood. Wild beasts won't come near a fire."

Asher heard the crack of twigs being hastily broken. He had no time to lose now. Busy stoking their fire, the two might not notice his motions. Raising himself on his hands, he shoved himself backward. Then, leaping to his feet, he turned and ran.

"Halt there!" he heard a voice yell. At the same instant a dagger, sailing past his cheek, sank shuddering into the ground ahead of him. Asher snatched it up. One less weapon in his back, he thought. Behind him he heard the rattle of pebbles as the two scrambled up the hill after him. He swung to his right, making toward the grove of cedars. A stone whistled past him. And another.

Evidently the men had given up the chase and were now venting their anger by throwing rocks at him. Asher, after running on a bit farther, halted to look behind him. The two were standing below him on the edge of the road; he could barely make them out. Seeing him turn, they raised their fists and bellowed curses. Asher could not restrain himself. Flourishing the dagger above his head, he broke into wild laughter. He felt safe and free. But would they seek him out if he returned to his flock? Did he dare go back to his sheep? He had learned the strangers' secret. They knew, or at least could well imagine, that he had overheard their conversation and could warn the prophet that the queen had sent two murderers to kill him. Nevertheless, he must now protect his flock from the wolves. He ran on.

He found his sheep safe, but though he searched through the huddled flock he failed to find the little goat. She was missing. Probably even then the two wild beasts were fighting over her dead body. But she had saved his life and saved his sheep, too.

It was no time now to mourn her loss. Asher quickly herded the flock into a deep ravine where they would be safe for the night. From an overhanging ledge he would watch over them, and watch, too, for the two cutthroats who might come searching for him.

Darkness had now come, but a full moon had risen and bathed the whole desolate region in yellow light. In the distance he heard an owl hooting. Below him in the ravine the occasional bleating of a lamb broke the stillness.

Once during the night he thought he heard the mumble of voices, though he realized it might have been his own sleepless brain playing tricks on him. But just before dawn the two strangers appeared in view, and this time it was no illusion. Silhouetted against the gray morning sky, they stood together on the crest of the hill, scrutinizing the landscape. One of them carried the club Asher had left behind him when he fled. The other held a dagger ready for action. For a long time they stood there, like evil shadows against the morning sky. Then, grumbling a final curse, they turned and went on their way.

Later that morning Asher returned to their camping site. The ashes of their fire were cold. Poking around among them, he discovered the charred fragments of cloth. Examining a piece, Asher wondered what it was that they had burned so carefully before they left.

2. THE MISSION TO
BETHABARA

ALL THE NEXT DAY Asher was tormented by doubts, by
fears, and by his own sense of duty. He realized that he
should go at once to warn the Baptist that a pair of
murderers, hired secretly by Herodias, were prowling
among his followers, watching silently for a chance to
do their bloody work. Asher puzzled over how he could
safely leave his flock and hasten to Bethabara. As the
day wore on, however, the less he felt like going. What
right had he, he asked himself, to abandon his sheep
and place them—and himself, too—in mortal danger?
After all, the new prophet, who had been preaching
for only a few months, was hardly more than a name to
him. Why should he endanger his life—and his sheep—
for a wild man whom he had never seen? And if he
should take himself to Bethabara, the queen's two
henchmen could easily spot him and close his mouth
forever with one of those fancy Phoenician tricks of
theirs. Had they not already proved their skill by nearly
driving a dagger through his back?

And besides all this, perhaps Herod was justified in being concerned about this Baptist, this young prophet who was stirring up the people and threatening the safety of the government. Perhaps Herodias, too, had excellent reasons for her hatred. Wasn't it wiser—and safer—to forget the prophet and let the two hired murderers do their work? Received as converted Essenes by the Baptist, they could go to the lonely wilderness where John dwelled and no man would ever know whose knife it was that struck. And if Asher himself kept his mouth closed and blabbed the story to no one, no one would ever be able to accuse him of having shirked his duty. Yes, Asher thought, let fate take its course. His duty was closer at hand.

"Tend your sheep, Asher, my boy," he muttered to himself. "Forget Bethabara and the prophet. The world beyond these pastures is an evil place. Let it go its way." He shrugged his shoulders.

So the whole day passed, while Asher fought back his conscience and silenced it. Yet back in the shadows of his mind there prowled, like the dark murderers themselves, a black feeling of guilt.

Toward evening, a gentle family of Galileans, bound for Bethabara from their distant home in the north, stopped to ask him where they could find water, just as so many other pilgrims had done. They were tired and thirsty after a day of travel and their supply of water had long since been exhausted.

"Every good shepherd knows where the brooks and

wells are," the father of the family said. "Lead us beside the still waters."

Asher, always glad to have friendly company, led them to the hidden well where he watered his sheep each noon. Then he stood watching as they filled their water skins and drank.

There were four of them—father, mother, and two young people. One was a boy of about twelve, the other a girl near Asher's own age. Asher had not seen a girl for many weeks, and he found it hard to keep himself from staring at her dark eyes with their long lashes, her white teeth, and the playful smile on her lips as she looked at him. He offered to pour water into her cupped hands and was about to compliment her on the delicate way she drank when her father spoke.

"My name is Zaccheus," he said. "And this is my daughter Deborah. We're on our way to Bethabara to hear the prophet. Is it still far?"

"Too far to reach before night," Asher said, hoping the family would stay as his guests under the stars. "It's a hilly road, and dangerous. You'd better stay the night here. You won't find it too uncomfortable sleeping on the grass."

Zaccheus smiled. "I know," he said. "I was a sheepherder once myself. My family is tired. Perhaps we had all better share the stars with you."

Asher was delighted. He led them to a sheltered nook between two boulders. Then, while Deborah and her mother unpacked their simple belongings and made supper ready, Asher answered the questions Zaccheus asked about the Baptist. Reports of John's message, his news that the kingdom of God was at hand and that the Messiah was coming, had already reached far north into Galilee, had even penetrated into the little town of Nain where Zaccheus and his family lived. They had heard rumors of the prophet and were making a pilgrimage, not through curiosity but because some word, some phrase of John's that had been repeated to them had set their imaginations on fire.

"We hear that there's been no prophet like him since Malachi," Zaccheus said. "They say he's another Elijah."

Then he asked Asher about the ceremony of baptism John had introduced—how he dipped converts into the waters of the Jordan in his baptism of repentance.

Asher told all he knew. He had seen and talked to many returning pilgrims, and he described how they seemed like different people after they had heard John's message and been baptized. He told the family, too, about the Baptist himself, how young and strong he was.

"They tell me," Asher said, "that once he picked up a wolf that had attacked him and pitched it headfirst into the middle of the Jordan. He's a match for anyone in strength—a young lion."

"I understand," Zaccheus remarked, "that Herod himself fears this young lion who's stirring up the people."

"I know right well he does!" Asher exclaimed. "And the queen hates him, too!"

Before he knew it, and in spite of his resolution to

tell no one, Asher found himself blurting out the whole story of his strange encounter with the queen's two henchmen. The family, seated around him on the grass, listened in horror to his story. Plots like the one Asher described were unknown in the village where they lived. Such treachery existed for them only in folk tales and in palaces.

"And you haven't yet warned the prophet!" Zaccheus exclaimed when Asher had finished his story. "But it's a crime itself to keep the knowledge from him! Why have you waited?"

"How could I go?" Asher asked as he waved his hand toward the flock, huddled now under the twinkling stars. "My sheep! The chief shepherd would fire me if I left them."

For several moments Zaccheus remained silent. Finally he looked at Asher. "Would it take long to reach Bethabara and return?" he asked. "Could you do it in a day?"

"I suppose so," Asher said dubiously. Then he paused a moment as a shadowy picture of the two murderers crossed his mind. "But I'm not planning to go."

"You're not?" Zaccheus asked. "Even if I offered to tend your sheep here while you're gone?"

"They'd never stay quietly with a strange shepherd." Asher was on the defensive.

"I'm an old hand at it. My family would help."

Asher thought a moment. "Why couldn't you warn the prophet yourself?" he asked. "You'll be there to-morrow."

"Certainly," Zaccheus replied. "Certainly I could warn him, and I'd make haste to do so. But how could I describe these two men so they'd be recognized?"

"The way I have to you. As two Essenes in white robes. That ought to be simple enough."

"And do you think these two vipers are simple-minded enough not to shed their disguise, knowing that anyone could point them out to the prophet? No, my son, it's your duty to run them down."

"Maybe," Asher said, shrugging his shoulders. "But it all sounds too involved and difficult. I think I'd better stay here with my sheep."

There was a long silence. Asher did not dare look into anyone's eyes. He knew that they were all staring at him, and he studied the end of his staff. He realized that he was talking like a coward, but he decided that if Zaccheus should accuse him of cowardice to his face, he would get up and go away. They could save the prophet's life themselves if they were so concerned about him.

But Zaccheus was too wise and knowing to alienate Asher for good by making the accusation. He changed his tactics.

"Would you agree to take my daughter Deborah and her mother to Bethabara while I tended the sheep here with my son?" he asked. "They're impatient to meet friends there, and they'll need your protection."

Asher looked up and found Deborah watching him with her dark eyes. He realized that she was disappointed in him, that she was beginning to think that in

spite of his strong arms and flashing eyes he was as
timid as one of the sheep he was so determined to
defend.

"But what would he protect us from?" she said with a
pert little laugh. "Our husky shepherd doesn't seem
very daring."

Asher felt his face go red. He started to rise and
leave. He hadn't invited the family to stay there so they
could sit around and insult him. But then he glanced at
Deborah and saw in her laughing eyes not so much a
criticism as a challenge—a challenge to show whatever
manhood he had in him. He felt the warm blood of
courage surge through his heart. He reached down and
touched the serpent-headed hilt of his dagger.

"Good enough!" he exclaimed. "I'll go with them tomorrow!" He turned to Deborah. "Will you be ready to
go with me at dawn?" he asked.

Deborah laughed gaily. "Of course I will!"

That night the family slept under the stars. Asher lay
a little distance apart, but all night he dreamed of Deborah. Her fingers were covered with all the queen's
rings, and she handed him a fiery sword to slay two
white snakes that had come out of a golden egg. . .

When he awoke, the family was already stirring. It
was a cool morning and so crystal clear that Mount
Nebo, towering many miles to the south, seemed hardly
a stone's throw away. Breakfast was soon over, instructions given, farewells said, and before the sun had burst
unheralded over the eastern hills, Asher, Deborah, and
her mother were on their way to Bethabara.

For a long while Asher walked ahead to show his independence. At his waist, hanging from his belt, he wore the dagger he had taken from the two cutthroats. He was still a bit ashamed of himself for appearing so cowardly the night before. Even now, sudden waves of fear rippled up and down his spine. He wondered what would happen if by chance he came face to face with the two killers. Would he be quick enough on the draw? Would he be able to last more than a few seconds with a pair of professional swordsmen? He tried not to think of these problems. The Baptist needed him. And Deborah, too.

Suddenly he heard her voice calling to him from behind. He whirled around, thinking that perhaps she was in trouble. He found her smiling. Behind her in the distance, beneath a tree, sat her mother fanning herself with a palm leaf. Asher strode back to the girl.

"What's the trouble?" he asked.

"I was afraid you'd get too far ahead," she explained. "Besides, I wanted to talk."

"About what?"

"Oh, about the weather, about Mount Nebo, about the landscape—about you."

"I'm not worth talking about!" Asher burst out. "You think I'm a coward, a bleating sheep, don't you?"

"I didn't say that," Deborah protested. "I only said that you didn't seem very daring."

Asher took her chin in his hand and roughly turned her face up toward his own. He looked deep into her eyes. "You'll soon know better," he said through clenched teeth. "You'll know better about my being daring before I'm through with this. And with you."

"Don't!" Deborah exclaimed as she pushed his hand away. "Don't! You're hurting me. And, besides, I hardly know you at all."

Asher seized her wrist and shook it. "Listen!" he said. "Before I get through, you'll know me better than any other man in the world. And don't think you won't."

Then he turned on his heel and strode off along the road.

But at the turn, not too far ahead, she found him waiting for her.

Well before noon the three reached the main highway leading to the ford at Bethabara. They no longer had the road to themselves, for the ford was the great stepping-off place leading to the Far East. It lay almost on the edge of the Syrian desert, which one must cross to reach Arabia and the distant and mysterious lands of India. Donkey trains laden with African wheat, caravans of camels bearing merchandise, plodded along the highway.

After waiting for one of the long caravans to pass with its dust and its shouting camel drivers, Deborah, her mother, and Asher joined a group of pilgrims who, like themselves, were on their way to hear the prophet. They, too, were friendly Galileans. Learning that Asher tended sheep nearby, they showered him with questions about the Baptist.

Asher told them all he knew, though their excitement at nearing Bethabara kept them from listening any too carefully to what he had to tell. They were now passing tents of goatskin and rude shelters of palm branches in which pilgrims from every section of Palestine lived while they listened to John the Baptist's preaching.

Noticing that the pair of donkeys the Galileans had with them were laden down with equipment, Asher asked if they had brought a tent along with them. They said they had and at once offered to share their shelter. Asher thanked them for the offer. He explained that he had to start back to his sheep before nightfall, but he would feel better about leaving the two women if the good Galileans would take care of them until their menfolk appeared.

"But you're not staying to hear the prophet?" one of the Galileans exclaimed.

"I have to tend my sheep," Asher confessed. "I have to hurry back."

"But you'll return?"

Asher glanced at Deborah. Her dark eyes met his and held them. He watched as her soft mouth parted and silently formed the word "Yes."

"Yes!" Asher exclaimed. "Yes, I'll be back. I'll find your tent and hear the preacher with you."

Then he smiled at Deborah.

Not far from the banks of the Jordan they found a grove of willows to camp in. After Asher had helped the Galileans to pitch their tent, he said good-by to Deborah and left them. It was his job now to find the prophet and deliver his message of warning.

It was no easy task to find him. Goats, dogs, wailing

children who had lost their parents, groups of men excitedly discussing the coming of the Messiah, women carrying water jars on their shoulders, Bedouins squatting before their tents, Sadducees, publicans, even a few finely dressed Pharisees—pilgrims of every description—thronged the banks of the river. But, for all the swarming hundreds, Asher could discover no one who knew where he could find John the Baptist.

"Off there," they would tell him, waving in the direction of the desert. "Every afternoon he suddenly appears out of nowhere. Wait patiently. You'll see him."

But Asher knew he couldn't wait patiently. That evening he had to start back to his flock, and besides, who knew what murderous plot the two agents of Herodias had already cooked up? But where were they? Nowhere among the crowds had he caught a glimpse of their white robes. His search was disheartening.

He wandered about disconsolately, inquiring hopelessly of everyone he met where he could find the prophet. He was about ready to give up the task and wait until the prophet appeared when a small, mangy dog trotted up to him, wagging his tail. Asher stooped down to give the friendly creature a pat. As he did so, a boy in ragged clothing and worn sandals came up and stood looking at him. Asher glanced up.

"You look like a bright boy," he said. "Maybe you can tell me something. Where can I find John the prophet?"

"You mean the big man who preaches and lives alone?"

"That's the one," Asher exclaimed as he stood up and

put a hand on the boy's shoulder. "I've got a message for him."

"I'm not supposed to tell," the boy said. "I've been told not to. But I'll show you where he stays. Follow me."

With the dog trotting ahead of them as if he knew the way, Asher and the boy hurried along a rocky path leading up toward the hills. Asher was still uncertain that he was on the right track, but at least the boy seemed more positive than anyone else he had met. As they walked along, Asher questioned him. "Aren't nosy pilgrims always after you to show them where the prophet lives? Don't some of them try to get you to take them there?"

"Oh, sometimes," the boy replied. "Yesterday two men even offered me money."

Asher stopped short. "Were they dressed in white?" he asked.

The boy looked surprised at the question. "No," he said. "They were dressed like you."

"And did you show them?"

The boy shook his head. "Why should I? My dog didn't like them."

"Dogs are smarter than some people," Asher remarked, thankful that the dog had liked him. "And what did the men do when you refused?"

"They went away."

Asher quickened his pace. The information the boy had just confided made it even more urgent to see the prophet and warn him. There could be only one reason why the queen's two killers were trying to find out where the prophet stayed. Moreover, Asher now understood why his search for white clothes had been fruitless. Zaccheus had been right. The hired murderers had shed their disguise and burned it in the fire.

Suddenly the boy halted and touched Asher's arm. "Look!" he said. "There he comes!"

Asher looked up the path.

An enormous man was coming toward them. Clad in a simple coat of camel's hair and a leather girdle, his arms and legs bronzed by the desert sun, he was striding toward them down the hill as if he were swept along on the wings of the wind. He was about thirty and bearded. His hair, yellow-red like the color of desert sand itself, flamed on his bare head in tongues of fire. A group of half a dozen men followed some distance behind.

Asher and the boy waited as the prophet, swinging along in huge strides, came toward them. Asher had never before seen so huge a man. When the prophet finally halted before them, towering above them both, Asher was speechless.

The prophet smiled at the boy and then turned to Asher. His dark eyes studied the young shepherd's face for an instant as if he could read there all that Asher knew.

"You have something to say to me?" he asked.

"Yes, Master," Asher stammered. "It's a warning."

"Speak up!" John said. "Have no fear."

Stumbling over his words, Asher recited his story.

"They're killers," he said as he finished. "And the boy has already seen them here."

The Baptist thought a moment. "Do you know who sent them?" he asked. "Are they agents of Herod?"

"Not these two," Asher answered. "These two were sent in secret by the queen, by Herodias herself."

"Herodias!" John's face darkened at the name. "They mean evil, then."

"They mean to kill you," Asher said. He touched the hilt of his serpent-headed dagger. "They came armed with these."

John glanced at the weapon. "So her tongue has now become a sharp sword!" He laid his hand on Asher's shoulder. "Many thanks, young man, for the warning. But do not let it trouble you. My time has not yet come." Then, turning, he gestured to one of the disciples, who were waiting in silence some distance away. A tall young man with fair hair came up to him. "Andrew," said John, "the young man here brings some disturbing news. It may require action. Let him tell you his story."

For a moment John again studied Asher's face; then, smiling at him, he swung around and, followed by the group of disciples, strode off down the hill.

With the boy and his dog trotting along beside them, Asher repeated all the details of the story to Andrew. The young disciple listened attentively but said nothing for some time after Asher had finished. Along the river Asher could see the throngs gathering around the great rock, shaped like a ship's prow, from which John preached. He had never before seen so large a crowd of men and was wondering vaguely if Herodias' two hirelings were prowling among them, when Andrew began outlining a plan the three were to follow. The boy was to help, too, for he had seen the two men and could probably recognize them if he saw them again.

The plan was a simple one. Before they reached the crowd, Andrew explained, they were to separate, but not so far apart as to lose sight of one another. They would then mingle with the crowd, moving casually from one place to another, until one of them came across the two suspects. When that happened, Asher or the boy was to signal to Andrew, who would be watching, by raising a hand and pointing with the thumb to where the men stood. Then Andrew would move toward them.

"They must be watched," Andrew said as he ended his instructions. "Skilled assassins strike like lightning and out of nowhere. But take care," he added, "that they don't see you first."

The three joined the crowd gathered around John's preaching rock. Asher, eager to end the search, pushed his way through the throng, looking briefly into each man's face, and at the same time being careful not to lose sight of Andrew, whose yellow hair showed plainly above the crowd. Occasionally Asher caught a glimpse of the boy carrying his dog and wandering about as if he were looking for a place to stand.

Asher had believed that the search would be a short one, but he soon realized that it was no simple matter to find a face he recognized among so many hundreds. Lost in the crowd, he was resting a moment, wishing that he had never agreed to go on the hopeless quest, when he heard a voice whispering in his ear. He was about to squirm around when he felt, just below his left shoulder blade, the sharp point of a knife pressing into his back.

"Stand still," the voice was whispering. "Must I stab you here?"

Asher stiffened. He stared straight ahead of him, hardly daring to twitch a muscle.

"Clear out of this crowd," the voice continued. "Get out fast and stay out. This knife is waiting."

Getting a grip on himself, Asher, his elbow close to his rigid body, slowly raised his hand high enough for Andrew to see it and pointed behind him at the assassin whose knife now jabbed deeper into his flesh.

"Do you hear me?" the voice whispered, so close now that Asher could feel the hot breath on his neck.

The knife dug deeper. Another inch, Asher thought, and it would reach his heart. He felt like crying out, like yelling "Murder!" But he merely nodded his head.

The knife was abruptly withdrawn, but an instant later he felt it slash his leather girdle, felt a deft hand slip girdle and dagger from his hip. He stood motionless, tense, expecting at any moment to feel the knife again. A long minute passed. Slowly turning his head, he again signaled a message to Andrew. He saw Andrew move swiftly away. Taking a deep breath, he spun around.

Behind him, placidly fanning himself with a palm leaf, stood a plump man with a round face. At sight of Asher's terror, the man looked startled.

"What's the matter, lad?" he asked.

Asher could not answer. Gritting his teeth, he pushed his way through the crowd. One thought controlled him now. He must get out of it, he must get back to his sheep, he must stay away even if he never saw Deborah again.

Detaching himself from the crowd, he started at a swift walk toward the main highway. Beneath his left shoulder blade he felt the slow, warm trickle of blood, but it did not stop him. Wounded and without a weapon, he marched on, his jaw set, his fists clenched.

He hadn't proceeded for more than fifty paces, however, when he heard behind him a deep murmur rise from the crowd, a deep murmur like the sound of the sea. In spite of himself, Asher slowed his pace. Should he take a last look, he wondered. One last look before he hit the dangerous road toward home. He turned.

John the Baptist, the prophet, the herald of the long-awaited Messiah, had mounted the rock and now stood there, his huge bronzed arms raised high above his fiery head.

"Prepare ye the way of the Lord," Asher heard John's great voice thunder. "Make his paths straight."

Spellbound, his wound forgotten, his fears eased, Asher stood listening to the Baptist's words.

3. TERROR ON THE PATH

IT WAS DIFFICULT for Asher to tear himself away even when John had stopped preaching. For a long time he stood staring at the vacant rock on which the Baptist stood. His deep, vibrant voice still thundered in Asher's ears. People pushed past him, but Asher, leaning against the fig tree where he had stood listening, hardly saw anyone.

He realized that much of what the prophet had said was beyond his depth. He had been raised an orphan and hadn't received the religious instruction that Jewish fathers usually gave their sons. But he had at least understood that John was urging his listeners to repent their sins and be baptized. He understood, too, that repentance meant something more than being sorry for one's sins: repentance must bear fruit in better lives. As John had said, the kingdom of God was at hand, a Messiah was coming who would lead the children of Israel into salvation. One must prepare one's life for the coming.

Asher tried hard to understand about the Messiah, about this Coming One who, John had said, was mightier than he, the laces of whose shoes he wasn't worthy to untie. The Messiah, Asher knew, had long been expected by the Jews, but now John was announcing that his coming was close at hand, that he was to appear, not in some future age, but in a few months, a few weeks, perhaps tomorrow. It was thrilling news, and Asher wished that he understood more of John's message.

But though he had not understood everything, Asher had felt the power of the preacher. John's voice, his blazing eyes, the powerful gestures of his arms, lifted the multitude, swept them along like a spring torrent carrying everything before it. Asher could understand now why the pilgrims seemed like different people when he had seen them returning from John's preaching and baptism. He understood why the news of this preacher had spread through Palestine like running fire. And he understood, too, why Herod feared his power and why Herodias hated and feared him.

Asher was eager to hear more; he wanted to stay and listen, but he realized that he must leave. He had his sheep to tend and he had promised Deborah's father that he would return as soon as he had delivered his warning to the Baptist. He had a long journey ahead of him, a journey that would take a whole night to make. It was a dangerous one, too, for now he had no weapon except the shepherd's sling he wore at his belt.

He must get started. The crowd was rapidly dwindling. Evening was coming. Asher, moving away from the tree, felt a twinge of pain beneath his left shoulder blade. He had almost forgotten that hardly an hour ago the point of a dagger had prodded deep into the flesh above his heart. He paused a moment wondering if the wound was serious.

He stepped out from under the tree but immediately dodged back. Coming toward him along the road was a pair he had instantly recognized. He had had no time to see their faces. It was their stride he had recognized —the swift, deadly, intent stride of the two killers.

Hardly daring to peer out from the protective trunk of the tree, Asher waited. He could hear the murmur of the killers' voices as they approached. The older one was speaking. His voice was crisp with anger, but Asher could not make out the words until the two had come abreast of him. Even then they passed by so swiftly that he caught only a few phrases. But they were enough.

"You Jewish thickhead!" the older one was saying. "You should have cut him down where he stood. Now he has ratted through our hands. We must strike at once!"

Then they were gone. Asher waited a moment. But as he stepped from behind the tree a dark figure, beaked like a hawk, swept past. The figure was so intent, so stealthy in his movement, that Asher stood breathless, watching. A short distance away the figure halted and, whirling about, stood for a moment staring at him. Then, turning swiftly, it went on.

Asher stood rooted to the spot, awe-stricken by his close escape. Had he stepped from behind the tree a moment sooner, the two killers would have slashed him into silence before he could have raised a hand to defend himself. At the very thought of it his heart began pounding. Cold sweat gathered on his forehead and he wiped it hastily away with his sleeve. For a moment he stood staring around him, bewildered, terrified. Then an icy wave of panic swept through him.

He started running. He felt that he must get away from Bethabara with its killers, its plots, its violence. Gasping for breath, his wound throbbing with every jolting stride he took, he ran blindly along the road toward home. Darkness was beginning to fall. Across the Jordan shadows were huddling in the clefts of the jagged hills. Soon he had left behind him the little huts of palm branches the pilgrims lived in during their stay. He ran on, one thought only in his mind—to join his peaceful flocks. In the distance a lone jackal howled.

Suddenly he halted. Above the western hills hung the evening star. Like a man waking from a nightmare, Asher stared at it. Serene, steadfast, pure, it glowed above the darkening hills like a star of hope—and a challenge. Asher felt its power. Stars are language to a shepherd, a form of speech, and Asher understood what the challenge meant. It was the challenge of a new faith, of the new faith John the Baptist had raised above the bleak hills of Palestine. Gazing with fixed attention at the star, Asher felt his mind clear, his emotions anchored and steadied. Slowly the tumult in his mind ceased and at the same instant the words of John, speaking from his rock, came back to him like an echo: "Bring forth fruits worthy of repentance!"

Asher looked at the road leading to Bethabara. "What fruit," he thought, "what fruit of repentance is this that I should flee when John is in mortal peril? Saving my own skin when the prophet's very life is in danger? Of what worth am I if I flee?" He glanced at the star again. "Yes," he said aloud. "I must give my life to John if he needs it. I must return!"

In the distance the jackal howled again.

Asher stooped down and snatching up the first stone his hand touched, he flung it with all his force toward the beast's hopeless cry. Then turning on his heel, he started for Bethabara.

The trip was long and painful, for his wound had begun to throb with every heartbeat. Asher realized that it needed dressing urgently and he realized, too, that it was fast becoming too dark for him to locate the prophet that evening in the lonely wilderness where he dwelled. He made his way toward the tent under the willows where he had left Deborah and her mother.

"I've returned," he announced as they greeted him. Then before they could ask him questions: "Zaccheus must wait awhile. The prophet needs me."

It was Deborah who noticed that he was in pain.

"You're pale, Asher!" she said as she studied his face. "What's happened?"

"It's a wound," Asher tried to pass it off. "It doesn't bother."

Deborah reached for the lamp. "But your cloak's bloody!" she exclaimed. "Asher, what happened?"

"I'll tell you later," Asher grumbled. "It's nothing."

But she insisted on dressing it and immediately got clean cloths and water. Then while her mother held the lamp, for her old fingers were too stiff and awkward to perform the operation, Deborah with gentle fingers washed off the clotted blood and bound up the wound. Asher sat patiently on the floor, doing his best to ward off Deborah's questions. He changed the subject by asking Deborah about distant Galilee.

"You must visit us," Deborah said. "You'd like it there. No one ever gets stabbed in my country—at least in Nain, no one does." Then she described Galilee to him. "You must see it in the spring. It's all budding pomegranates and poppy-red anemones and cyclamen of all colors. And you must see Mount Tabor at sunrise and hear our turtledoves calling to each other."

"It sounds wonderful," Asher said. "But before I go there I must hear more about the new kingdom the prophet talks about. And there's a question, too, I want to ask him."

"What sort of a question?" Deborah asked.

"It sounds funny perhaps, but I want to ask him how a person prays. They say he teaches people how to pray and I want to learn."

Deborah laughed. "That *is* a funny question!" she exclaimed. "Don't you know already?"

"No," Asher said irritably. "I don't. I've tried to pray and I don't seem to know how. I was never taught anything except how to tend sheep. I guess I must be ignorant. I must learn."

"My father will teach you. He knows all about prayers."

"I must ask the Baptist," Asher said obstinately. "Or Andrew."

"Do as you please," Deborah said. "But whatever else you learn, learn how not to get stabbed again."

"It wasn't my own fault," Asher grumbled. "And now haven't you finished?"

"Except for your bad temper you're almost as good as new," Deborah said as she patted him on the shoulder. "And now get up and put on your shirt."

Asher clambered to his feet and pulled on his shirt. "I must see the Baptist before daybreak," he said as he reached for his cloak.

"But where can you stay tonight?" Deborah asked as she glanced around the little tent.

Asher laughed. "A shepherd, you ought to know, prefers the stars. I'll find a good star to sleep under, don't worry."

After bidding Deborah and her mother good-night, he found a comfortable spot under a willow and curled up; with his wound dressed and no longer painful, he soon fell asleep.

Hours later Asher awoke to find someone bending over him and calling his name. He sat up, startled. Dawn was breaking, and in the dim light he saw Zaccheus standing before him. For an instant Asher imagined he was back among his sheep. But then he remembered.

"Zaccheus!" he exclaimed. "How do you happen to be here? Who's caring for my sheep?"

Zaccheus mumbled a prayer. "A misfortune has befallen you, Asher," he said. "And it's my fault because you came here to Bethabara at my urging."

"My sheep have gone astray? They're lost?"

Zaccheus shook his head. "No, my son. It's not your sheep that's lost. It's your job as shepherd."

Asher guessed what had happened. "The chief herder . . . " he began.

Zaccheus nodded. "Early this evening the chief shepherd arrived with two others. When he saw you were missing and had gone to Bethabara, he fell into a fury."

"Did you tell him why I had come here?"

"Yes, but that only increased his rage. He'd never heard of the prophet and vowed he'd thrash you black and blue."

"He would," Asher said as he rose to his feet. "But I must get back there."

"Nay," said Zaccheus. "You'll stay here with us. Have you a family?"

"None," Asher said.

"You'll stay with us then," Zaccheus repeated. "And after we have heard the prophet, you'll return with us to Nain. I can use you in my olive grove."

Asher stood thinking. "I must see the Baptist before I can do anything," he said. "Did you say the chief shepherd was not alone?"

"He had two Moabites with him. Old sheepherders. You needn't worry. Will you stay?"

Asher reached down for his cloak. He looked into the old man's kindly face. "Yes," he said. "I'll stay with you. But now I must hasten to see the Baptist or one of his disciples."

Without further words with Zaccheus, Asher hurried away. In the gathering light he soon found the path the young boy with the dog had shown him. But he had not gone for more than a mile along it when he noticed three men ahead of him clustered around what appeared to be a heap of rags.

Asher approached. He soon realized that it was something more than a bundle of loose rags that lay there, for a pair of sandaled feet protruded from it. At one side a thin trickle of blood had formed a pool on the rocky path. But what instantly caught Asher's eye and held it was the hilt of a dagger protruding from the corpse. It had been driven through the dead man's back in so swift and powerful a thrust that hardly an inch of steel showed beneath the hilt.

Asher stared at the weapon with rising horror. It wasn't the skill and violence of the blow that set his heart pounding or drained the blood from his face. It was the hilt itself. Were a thousand daggers shown him, Asher could never have mistaken this one. Even in pitch darkness his hand would recognize its serpent-shaped hilt.

Hardly daring to ask the question, Asher turned to

the three men standing in silence several paces away.
"Who is it?" he asked, his voice trembling with excitement. "In God's name, who is this man?"

The three men shifted their eyes from the corpse and
stared at Asher. One of them shrugged his shoulders.

"Has no one looked?" Asher asked. "Has no one looked
at the dead man's face? He might be . . ." He paused,
not daring even to finish the sentence.

One of the men spoke. "Who wishes to defile himself
by touching a dead body?" he said.

Asher glanced at the corpse. Flies were already buzzing over the little pool of half-dried blood. Rubbing
the palms of his hands downward on his robe, Asher
stepped closer to the body. Little as he knew of Jewish
law, he realized that touching a corpse made a man un-
clean, a defilement that must be removed by ceremonial washings and prayer. But his fear that it might be
someone he knew, that it might be one of John's disciples, or even John himself, overcame his repugnance.

He kneeled down by the body. The dead man's
clothes had been drawn over his face. Gently, carefully,
so that he would touch no more than was necessary,
Asher took the cloth between thumb and finger and
slowly drew it back. Behind him he heard the men
murmuring, aghast at what he dared do.

He pulled the cloth away a little more. It caught on
something beneath the head, and Asher had to jerk it
free. The robe fell back suddenly from the face, and
Asher, with a loud cry, sprang backward.

"It's the old one!" he shouted as he stared in horror at the face. "It's one of them!"

He swung around and then gazed about him in bewilderment.

Swiftly and stealthily, the three men had disappeared.

4. THE ROMAN PRISON

ALONE WITH THE BODY, Asher hardly knew which way to turn. Should he notify the centurion who, he knew, was stationed in Bethabara with a cohort of soldiers to keep order among the throngs of pilgrims? Or should he, on the other hand, hasten with the news to Andrew?

After a moment's hesitation, he decided upon the latter course. Following the winding path over the hills, he continued until he came to a cliff. Above him he could see the dark openings of several caves. The boy had told him it was here that John the Baptist lived. Near the mouth of one of the caves Asher could see a group of men seated on the ground listening to a tall man—Andrew.

Asher scrambled up the path to the broad shelf of rock on which the men had gathered. As he reached them, Andrew glanced toward him. Panting with his exertions and excitement, Asher was about to shout out his news when Andrew gestured to him to be seated quietly with the others. Unwilling, but obedient, Asher sat down.

Andrew continued with his talk. He was addressing about twenty pilgrims who were to be baptized by John that afternoon. Andrew was explaining what the baptism meant.

"This is the baptism of repentance," Andrew was saying. "It is not merely a ceremonial washing. Only those of you who have repented and who plan to lead a new life will be received by John for baptism. John's baptism is a public confession of sin and a public pledge to lead a better life. You must put away your pride. You must become humble men who believe in the coming of the Messiah. In the words of John, my friends: Repent ye, for the kingdom of heaven is at hand."

Asher sat listening. However, he had not long to wait, for after Andrew had uttered a brief prayer, he dismissed the group. Now, he said, each man was to have a word with the Baptist himself.

Led by another disciple, the group filed away toward the mouth of a cave above them. Andrew then came over to where Asher was sitting.

"What's the matter?" Andrew asked. "What has happened?"

"I've got strange news," Asher blurted out. "One of the hired killers has been stabbed."

"Which one?" Andrew asked.

"The older of the two," Asher said. "The one with the hooked nose. Stabbed with his own dagger."

"With his own dagger!" Andrew thought a moment.

"What does the psalmist say? 'The wicked have drawn out the sword, . . . to slay those who walk uprightly. Their sword shall enter their own heart.'" Then he glanced down the path. "They were likely on their way here, perhaps just before dawn. To do their bloody work while the Baptist was alone saying his prayers at sunrise. But show me where the body lies."

Together they set forth along the hilly path.

"But how do you happen to be back in Bethabara?" Andrew asked. "Didn't you return to your sheep?"

Asher explained what had brought him back. And he described, remembering that Andrew had not yet heard the story, how a knife had been pressed against his back while he was standing in the crowd and how the dagger had been taken from him.

"While I was standing there near you?" Andrew asked.

Asher nodded. "It was done so swiftly!" Then he told Andrew how he had seen the two killers later on. "They were being followed. A man with a face like a hawk trailed after them."

Andrew nodded. "They were being watched," he murmured. "The centurion . . ."

They had reached a bend in the path. Below them, far in the distance, lay the river Jordan, its deep and winding passage marked by a jungle growth of willows and oleanders, tall reeds and tamarinds. Along the banks Asher could see hundreds of tents, and willow and palm shelters, where the pilgrims lived during their stay to hear John's preaching. A faint hum of activity rose from the encampment.

For a moment Andrew halted. With a sweeping gesture of his arm, he drew Asher's attention to the numbers who had gathered at the Bethabara ford. "They have come from everywhere," he said. "From all the country of Judea and from all the region round about Jordan—and from Jerusalem. Too often men forget the power of the spoken word, but in a few brief months our Baptist has gathered this multitude. People of every calling and description have come here—the rich and the poor, the sweepings of the city's streets, the proud and the humble, the innocent and the wicked. Even Roman soldiers in Herod's cohorts have come and listened to John's message."

"Was it one of these Roman converts, perhaps, who killed him?" Asher asked as they made their way down the path.

"A Roman, perhaps," said Andrew, "but not a true convert. Herod has many spies here."

"But would one of Herod's spies dare kill an assassin hired by Herod's wife?"

"There is a dark mystery here," Andrew said. "A mystery that perhaps we can fathom. As you heard from the lips of the killers themselves, they were here in secret. We know that Herod Antipas fears our Baptist. He fears not only his power over the people but he fears him as a prophet. Men whose power is the sword live in awe of those whose power is the word.

It's a power they can't understand—a force whose mystery baffles and terrifies them."

"So Herod's fear of John might lead him to protect the Baptist's life?" said Asher in a flash of understanding.

"Herod has a greater fear of the Baptist dead than of the Baptist living, yes," Andrew agreed, smiling at the young shepherd. "He fears the anger of the people if John were killed."

"But his wife—Herodias?"

Andrew strode along the path in silence for a moment. "Who knows what secret reasons lurk in that evil heart? It's difficult to tell where hatred comes from, Asher. But our Baptist has publicly denounced Herodias, and to her face."

"For what?" Asher asked.

"For her marriage to Herod. She took her daughter Salome and, abandoning her husband, ran off with Herod, her husband's brother. To rob a father of his daughter is sin enough. But under Jewish law it's wickedness to steal your brother's wife. John has denounced this second marriage of Herodias to her very face. For this she has set herself against him. She desires his death."

"She may hate the Baptist because she feels guilty," Asher said. "Guilty of breaking up a home and robbing Salome of her real father."

"Who knows?" Andrew said. "Hatred has its roots in darkness. But they say Herod and Salome live in awe of Herodias. She has a strange power over both of them."

They had reached the crest of a hill and were starting down it when Asher suddenly stopped and stared ahead of him in alarm.

"The body's gone!" he exclaimed.

"It was lying near here?" Andrew asked.

Asher ran ahead and pointed to the brownish stains of blood on the path. "See! It was lying here!"

"And it was here you found him? It was here he was struck down?"

"From behind," Asher said. "And with his own dagger."

"Are you sure of that?" Andrew asked.

"I couldn't have mistaken the hilt. I'd held it myself. I showed it to you."

"It's a strange killing," Andrew said. "As if God's wrath itself had struck him down. But where can the other one be?"

"They were together when I saw them last," Asher said. "The older one was raging because his partner hadn't killed me in the crowd."

For a while Andrew stood staring thoughtfully at the stain of blood. "Return to your friends, Asher," he said finally. "And stay among them. Don't venture forth. I will send you word or come to you myself when I have learned something about this murder. And now make haste."

"I'll try to obey," Asher said.

Andrew raised his hand and was about to start back

toward the cliffs when he paused. "Another question," he said. "Did you show the dagger to anyone besides me?"

"I'm afraid many people could have seen it," Asher confessed. "I was a bit proud of carrying it."

"Take care," Andrew said. "And may God protect you."

He raised his hand again . . .

For several days Asher stayed among the Galileans, waiting impatiently for some word from Andrew. Though the disciple had not warned him to keep the matter secret, Asher told no one, not even Deborah, about the murder. But this made it difficult for him. She could not understand why he did not go to hear the prophet, particularly as he had half promised to go with her.

"You act as if you were afraid of something," she told him. "You act as if you were in hiding."

Asher shrugged his shoulders. "Perhaps I am," he said. "Who knows?"

Finally, on the third day when no word had come from Andrew, Asher decided he must hear the preacher. With John speaking so nearby, he could not remain in seclusion any longer.

"It's about time!" Deborah said when he told her. "You've been sitting around here long enough, twiddling your thumbs."

Asher flushed with anger. "You're unjust," he said. "I have reasons for staying hidden. But I'll take a chance. I want to hear the preacher."

"But why have you been so secretive? Even father has begun to wonder."

"You'll soon know," Asher said. "Please be patient."

"You're asking too much of me," Deborah remarked, pouting.

With Deborah and her family, Asher left the little huts of willow branches and walked along the margin of the Jordan toward John's rock. They were early, but the crowd had already assembled, waiting eagerly for the Baptist to appear. The sun was warm, for summer was rapidly approaching, when the Jordan valley would blaze with heat. Then John would move northward and perhaps continue his preaching beyond the deep valley, perhaps near springs and pools of water where he could baptize his converts.

Glancing about the crowd, Asher wondered if anyone was watching him, or if Andrew would see him. He felt disturbed by the thought that he was disobeying Andrew's command to stay hidden, but he felt that he might be forgiven if his reason for coming was to hear the Baptist. And what danger could there be? One of the assassins was dead, and the other one must be dead or in flight.

Standing quietly in the crowd, he waited with Deborah and her family until the Baptist appeared, towering like a bronze giant above the crowd. Asher listened. Again he felt himself being carried away, lifted out of himself by John's vibrant voice—the voice crying in the wilderness.

"O generation of vipers," John was saying, "who hath

warned you to flee from the wrath to come? Bring forth therefore fruits worthy of repentance, and begin not to say within yourselves, We have Abraham to our father: for I say unto you, That God is able of these stones to raise up children unto Abraham. And now also the axe is laid unto the root of the trees; every tree therefore which bringeth not forth good fruit is hewn down, and cast into the fire.

"I indeed baptize you with water; but one mightier than I cometh, the latchet of whose shoes I am not worthy to unloose: he shall baptize you with the Holy Ghost and with fire: Whose fan is in his hand, and he will thoroughly purge his floor, and will gather the wheat into his garner; but the chaff he will burn with fire unquenchable."

The "fire unquenchable"! The "wrath to come"! The words seemed to burn like fire itself. Asher, his body tense with listening, did not at first feel the rough hand laid abruptly on his shoulder. It was not until harsh fingers gripped the muscles of his arm that he became aware of the helmeted soldier who had silently pushed his way through the crowd toward him.

"Come along!" the soldier murmured as he jerked his head toward the rear. "You're wanted."

Startled, Asher stared at the soldier. Everything seemed to go empty inside him. He knew now why Andrew had warned him to remain hidden.

Instinctively aware that something unusual was going on beside her, Deborah looked around. A glimpse at Asher's face told her that he was in peril.

"I'm being taken," Asher murmured.

The soldier gripped Asher's arm by the wrist and twisted it behind his back. "Are you coming?" he muttered. "Quietly?"

"Asher!" Deborah said, reaching for him.

The soldier swung Asher around and shoved him rapidly through the crowd. Behind him Asher was aware of hearing John's voice—strong, resonant, fearless. Once again it gave Asher courage.

At the highway, three soldiers and an officer were waiting.

Asher was marched along the dusty road. People along the way stopped to stare at them. Finally they came to the barracks where the Roman soldiers were stationed to police the region and suppress any threat of a rebellion. For Herod, ruler of all Galilee and Perea in the name of Rome, feared John might whip the people into revolt.

Inside the barracks Asher was led to a small room. Two men were sitting behind a table. One was a centurion with a breastplate embossed with medallions. He was a burly man with a deep scar that ran from his cheekbone to one corner of his mouth. His blue eyes seemed shrewd and wise. The other was evidently an official but he wore no insignia. He had a lean, cruel face with eyes as sharp and as cold as steel. He studied Asher for a moment, his eyes wandering to Asher's girdle where he still carried his sling.

"You're a shepherd?" he asked.

Asher nodded. "From the hills on this side of the Jordan. My name is Asher, son of Isaac."

"Take it down," said the man with the lean face as he turned to a secretary who stood near him with a writing tablet.

As the official turned, Asher caught his face in profile and instantly recognized the man. He was the mysterious stranger he had seen following the two assassins. So, Asher thought even in his fright, the killers had been watched by Herod's men. The official stared at Asher with his sharp hawklike eyes. "What are you doing here away from your flocks?" he asked.

"I came to hear the Baptist, sir," Asher said.

"You came armed only with that sling?"

"I had a dagger with me then."

"Where is that dagger now?"

"It was taken from me," Asher began. "While I was standing listening to the prophet, someone sneaked up behind me . . ." He stopped. The mocking, incredulous glint in the cold eyes of his inquisitor made him realize how feeble the whole story sounded. He realized, too, that he was wading into deep water—the treacherous water Andrew had foreseen. "I would like to tell you the whole story, sir," he blurted. "I can explain . . ."

"We can hear that later," the official interrupted coldly. "Would you recognize this weapon of yours if you saw it?"

"It was not my weapon, sir," Asher began.

"You stole it?"

"It wasn't exactly stealing, sir. I only picked it up."

The inspector studied Asher with a sarcastic smile and then turned to the secretary who was recording Asher's answers. "Bring the dagger here," he ordered.

Asher watched hopelessly as the secretary slowly removed the linen wrapping from the weapon and laid it on the table.

"Is this the weapon?" the inspector asked.

Asher nodded. "Yes," he admitted. Then he burst out: "But I can prove I didn't use it. I can prove I wasn't guilty of the murder."

"So you know about it, eh?" the official said. "This murder?" He turned to the centurion. "Confront him with our chief witness."

The centurion spoke to one of the guards. A moment later a heavy oak door swung open. Asher, his arms hanging limply at his sides, stared dully at the tall man who entered the room. At first Asher did not recognize him. He seemed like a total stranger until he stepped forward out of the shadows and Asher could see his eyes. They were the eyes of a jackal. His narrow eyes on Asher, the man walked across the room. For a moment or two the younger of the two killers stared at Asher. Then he nodded.

"That's the man," he said. "The murderer."

"He's the shepherd who stole your friend's weapon?"

"Yes, and killed him with it—murdered my friend for the gold he carried."

"You're a liar!" Asher shouted. He turned to the centurion. "This man is a hired assassin, a dagger-man hired by her . . ."

In a flash the big man was on him, his enormous hands encircling Asher's throat. Asher tried to struggle, to strike out, but the huge hands tightened in a grip of iron. The room whirled before his eyes. He saw faces, heard shouting, felt someone tearing the hands loose. And then suddenly, with a burst of scarlet flame, everything went black.

5. THE COURAGE OF FAITH

ASHER'S ARREST had been so swiftly and expertly executed that only Deborah had been aware of what had taken place. She had caught sight of his startled face as the soldiers seized him. But the next moment, before she could even touch his hand or speak, he was gone.

Terrified by what had happened, she moved closer to her father's side and tried to tell him. But he was so intent upon the Baptist's preaching that he hadn't heard her. Making every effort to control herself, Deborah had remained silent until the preaching had ended. Then she grasped her father's arm.

"They've taken him away!" she whispered excitedly. "Asher's been arrested!"

"Asher? But when?"

"Not so long ago. Two soldiers pushed their way up to him and marched him off. I saw them do it."

Zaccheus looked worried. "Were they Roman soldiers?"

"They looked like it. One of them twisted his arm

61

behind his back and shoved him through the crowd. Why do they want Asher?"

Zaccheus said nothing for a while. He walked along beside Deborah, stroking his beard and glancing about him. "I'm afraid our friend Asher has got himself into deep water," he said finally.

"But what can we do to help him?" Deborah pleaded. "What should we do?"

"Nothing, for a while," Zaccheus said. "I must make careful inquiries. Meanwhile, we must keep to ourselves and say nothing."

By now they had reached their little camp under the willows. A group of pilgrims were waiting, for, after listening to the Baptist, they usually gathered there to discuss his preaching. These discussions often lasted until late at night and often there was disagreement and heated argument. Not all the pilgrims accepted John's doctrines; indeed, some of Zaccheus' friends found them blasphemous.

Lingering in the little shelter, Deborah waited until her father had become involved in the discussion. When the voices of the men, disputing beneath the trees, had risen, she slipped away. Running along the path by the river, she made her way toward the place where John baptized his followers. She knew that she would find Andrew there, and she was eager to tell him what had happened.

The sun was still shining and crowds of people lined the river banks, watching John, surrounded by his disciples, perform the strange ceremony of baptism.

Though it was in some respects an ancient custom, John had made it something new in Palestine. He stood waist deep in the milky, swirling water, his fiery head framed by the oleanders and tamarinds along the banks. One by one the converts came to him. Deborah, listening to the silky rustle of the stream as it flowed toward the Dead Sea, watched as John's powerful arms dipped them one by one into the waters of the river.

It was easy for her to recognize Andrew among the disciples. Asher had described him as tall and blond. But for her to go down to the edge of the bank and call to him, or even to speak to him when he came up the bank, required more courage than she possessed. For a long time she stood alone and though Andrew several times passed close to her, she did not, as a stranger and a woman, dare accost him.

Flustered and embarrassed, realizing that Asher's life might depend upon her bringing the news of his arrest to Andrew, still she faltered. Ashamed of her own timidity, she was about to wander away when Andrew, leading two women out of the water, their lank hair still dripping, caught sight of her. He came over.

"What's the matter?" he asked in his gentle voice. "You look frightened."

Deborah, more flustered than ever, only nodded.

"Tell me, child," Andrew said. "Did you come here to be baptized?"

Deborah shook her head. "I can't, unless my father permits me."

"But you're here for something. What is it?"

"It's about Asher!" Deborah found words at last and she poured out her story. "He was eager to hear the preaching," she said when she had finished. "Besides, I nagged and told him he was a sluggard and a coward. Can you help him?"

Andrew glanced toward the Baptist. He had finished his baptisms for the day and was now wading toward the shore, his bronze arms wet and glistening in the sunlight.

"We must tell your story to John," Andrew said.

"You tell him," Deborah pleaded. "I don't dare."

Andrew smiled and took her arm. He led her along the bank toward the Baptist, who was now surrounded by a swarm of people asking questions. Two Roman soldiers were among them and Deborah, frightened at seeing them there, was happy to have Andrew close beside her.

As they reached the group, Deborah heard someone ask if John himself could be the Messiah. It was a question that had evidently troubled many people, for Deborah had heard her father discuss it with his friends. She listened for John's answer.

"I baptize you with water," John replied, "but, as I have told you, the Messiah will baptize you with the Holy Spirit and with fire. I only prepare the way for him. I make the paths straight."

A richly dressed man spoke up. "How, Master, can I make my own path straight?" he asked.

John studied him for a moment. "You who have two coats," he said, "must share them with those who have none and you must share your food with those who are hungry."

"I am a tax collector," another member of the group put in. "What must I do before I can receive your baptism of repentance?"

John turned to him. "Collect only the amount of taxes that are due you," he said. "Accept nothing more than your legal fee."

Then one of the Roman soldiers pushed his way through the crowd. "My comrade here, and I," he said, "would like to know what soldiers must do to live a good life."

"You soldiers here in Palestine have special privileges under Roman law. Never abuse these privileges, rob no one, and bring no false testimony against people in the courts." Then John added, with a smile, "And don't grumble about your low pay."

When the questioning came to an end, Andrew led Deborah up to the Baptist. Standing in front of him now, quite close enough to touch him, Deborah became frightened all over again. Many times she had heard John preach. She had watched him as he stood addressing the great crowds. But then it had always seemed as if he were someone from a different world, as if he weren't made of flesh and blood like other men. And now he stood before her, with his wet hair and arms, smiling gently at her embarrassment and her blazing cheeks. She hardly dared raise her eyes to his when she heard him asking where she came from.

"From Nain in Galilee," she stammered. "We came to hear news of the Messiah."

"And this young shepherd you tell about—Asher—is from Galilee?"

Deborah felt mortified at knowing so little about the young man whose life she was trying to save. She shook her head. "I hardly know what country he comes from," she confessed. "But he came here to Bethabara at my father's urging, to give you warning."

"God sent him," John said. "God's messengers are not always angels. They sometimes come as shepherds. Was a centurion with the soldiers who arrested him?"

Deborah was puzzled. "I don't know what a centurion is," she admitted.

"An officer," John said. "He's in charge of the soldiers stationed at Bethabara. He's a friendly man. Andrew knows him and will speak to him about your friend Asher."

"And the centurion will set Asher free?"

John shook his head. "I can't promise you that. The centurion receives his orders and must obey them like any good soldier. Sometimes the orders are harsh ones, sometimes unjust, sometimes cruel. But it is a soldier's duty to obey, just as I must obey an inner voice from God."

He paused for a moment. "In Herod's court I have a bitter enemy who would see me dead. I have no fear of that. God has already struck down one enemy sent against me. God will continue to protect me until my mission here is done and the Messiah has appeared. It is only my disciples and my followers I must protect, and Asher is one of them. He has stepped in the path of my enemies and they may ride him down. They may try to destroy him for what he has already done for me and for what he knows. But I thought Andrew had warned the young man to keep hidden."

"I did, Master," Andrew said. "I told him to stay hidden. But he was eager to hear you preach."

"It was partly my fault," Deborah, summoning up her courage, managed to put in. "I nagged at him."

"Never worry about it," John said as he laid his hand on Deborah's shoulder. "I doubt if they will let Andrew see Asher. But he can speak to our friend, the centurion. Andrew will explain what Asher has done for us, and what he knows."

Then John, smiling, turned away. Again the crowd swarmed about him. Patiently, he continued answering their questions.

Andrew walked along with Deborah as she started toward home.

"Could I send Asher a message?" she asked.

"What is your message?" Andrew inquired.

"Will you send word to him," Deborah murmured, "that I'm proud of him?" She paused a moment. "And that I'm sorry."

"I will," Andrew said, and he stood watching as she hurried away along the Jordan path toward her family.

When Asher recovered consciousness, he found himself lying on the stone floor of a cell. Faintly he could recall being dragged there. He had no idea what hour of the day it now was. He could see that the sun was shining, for a beam of light, falling aslant through the barred window above his head, revealed the name, "Saraph the Moabite," scratched into the stone of the wall, and under it the words: "This day I die!"

It seemed as from a distance—though perhaps it was only in the next cell—he heard a voice complaining angrily. With returning consciousness, Asher could make out a few words. It was someone complaining bitterly to the jailer about being held a prisoner. Asher recognized the voice. It was that of the young killer! Asher struggled to his feet and put his ear to the wall.

"He promised to let me go," the voice whined. "After I identified the murderer, he promised to release me. I have work to do. I am a disciple of the prophet. I want to be baptized by the Dipper."

"Forget it," Asher heard a gruff voice saying. "You'll be baptized soon enough. Tomorrow. Or the day after."

"I have friends in Tiberias," the voice was whining again. "Powerful friends. This centurion will rue the day he ever locked me up." The young killer suddenly lowered his voice. "Listen," Asher heard him murmur. "I have money, plenty of it. Here! See this coin?"

"Bah! A shekel only."

"More if you wish. But look, comrade. Only show me the young shepherd's cell. I have some unfinished business with him. Put me in his cell for only a moment. Ten shekels! Show me his cell. My business with him will take only a moment."

Asher heard the jailer mumble something and the sound of his footsteps coming down the corridor toward him. He drew back to one corner of his cell and stood facing the door. For a moment he felt that the entire world had gone black, evil, murderous. There seemed to be no ray of light, no spark of goodness remaining in it. And now, perhaps, for money, the jailer was opening the door of his cell to a killer. Asher felt the sweat gathering in the palms of his clenched fists. The footsteps drew nearer, reached his door, halted for a moment before it, and then passed on.

Weak from the suspense, Asher dropped to his knees. Once before in an emergency he had tried to pray, but prayer hadn't come. But now he remembered something the Baptist had said when he had last heard him preaching: "A man can receive nothing, except it be given him from heaven." Asher clasped his hands in terror and raised his eyes toward the little window. Suddenly and without effort on his part a prayer rose to his lips, a prayer he recalled from one of the Psalms. "Let the sighing of the prisoner come before thee," Asher murmured. "According to the greatness of thy power preserve thou those that are appointed to die."

No sooner had he uttered the prayer than he felt the tension go, the terror vanish. He felt as if John's own great courage and manhood filled his little cell with warmth and light. Then, gathering his shepherd's cloak around him, he curled up in a corner and drifted off into a peaceful sleep, as if he were lying alone among his herd under the watchful stars.

But once during the night he was awakened by loud voices and the tramp of feet. He heard the voice of the young killer loudly asking where he was being taken.

"To be baptized!" a gruff voice answered with a sarcastic laugh. "You're getting dipped."

The tread of feet passed by his cell door.

The days dragged by. He soon lost count of how many times the patch of light had crawled along the wall toward the fateful words: "This day I die." Then early one morning—after weeks of waiting—the door opened, and Asher found the jailer standing outside it with two soldiers.

"Come out of there!" the jailer snarled. "They want to see you."

Picking up his cloak and wondering what was in store for him, Asher preceded the soldiers along a corridor to a bare room where the centurion sat at a table reading a report. He glanced up as the soldiers brought Asher in.

"Leave the young man here," he said curtly. "And wait outside." He continued reading. Finally he rolled up the sheet of parchment and tossed it before him on the table.

"I have called you here for two reasons," the centurion said. "The first is to tell you that you're being freed of the charge of murder. Under pressure, if it may be called that, the young fellow who tried to choke you in here confessed to having murdered his companion for calling him a Jew. That's the reason he gave, though the dead man's money might tell another story."

"The money he carried to pay for John's death?" Asher asked. He was convinced that the centurion knew about the plot to kill John, and the officer's quick response proved him right.

"Yes, but it bought his own. Evil has a way of biting back. So, my young friend, you're free. But now you face an even greater danger."

Asher was startled. "From what?"

"From Queen Herodias." The centurion beckoned to Asher to come closer. For a moment he sat drumming gently on the table. Then, in a low voice: "Herodias has evidently learned that you warned John of her plot to kill him. She believes, too, that it was you who murdered her assassin."

"But I'm innocent!" Asher exclaimed.

"I am convinced that you are. Andrew was here in your behalf and told me your story. You may be innocent of murder, but you are not innocent of having talked. Herodias fears you may talk again. Perhaps to Herod himself. She does not care to have her plot known, or to have it thwarted again. She is already angling for a pair of fresh cutthroats who'll not fail her this time. And she may close your mouth by her favorite means."

Asher felt his blood run cold. "But why am I the only one she thinks disclosed the plot? Perhaps the assassin himself, when he confessed killing his confederate, also confessed the plot to murder John."

"Not he! Since he botched the job himself, he fears Herodias more than he fears the law. Though he's still in prison, he lives in mortal terror of her. He knows that if he confessed he had been hired to kill the Baptist, he would not only have Herodias to reckon with but Herod as well. Herod does not want to see John killed."

"Why?"

"For many reasons. One is that Herod fears the people, the followers of John. He does not yet know about his queen's plot to murder the Baptist."

"No one has told him?"

"No one dares."

The centurion paused and picking up the roll of parchment studied the rolled end for a moment. "For John's sake, Herod must be told. He alone can curb his wife's thirst for blood."

"What can be done?" Asher exclaimed.

"I am a friend of Andrew's," the centurion continued, "and I have listened to John's preachings. I feel that he is bringing our Roman world a message that we must take to heart, else we will perish in our own blood. Are you willing to risk your life to save John, if I should help you?"

"I would be willing," Asher said. "Gladly. But how?"

"Since no one else dares to tell Herod of his wife's plot against the Baptist's life, you must do so."

"I!" Asher gasped. "But how could I tell him?"

"He will see you if I recommend it," the centurion said. "And there are others at court who will urge him to listen and who will vouch for your story. Do you remember the man who questioned you here?"

"The man who sat beside you?"

"Yes. He is in charge of Herod's spies and informers."

"Can he be trusted?"

"As far as any informer can be. Are you ready to go to the city of Tiberias, on the Sea of Galilee, to speak to Herod?"

"But how am I to get there?"

"I will send you with an armed guard. It will be a dangerous mission. Now is the time to refuse to go. There will be no turning back later. Refuse to tell the story of Herodias' plot and you may save your life. Tell it, and you may save John's."

"I'll go!" Asher exclaimed. "I'll tell my story to Herod!"

"I'll take your word," the centurion said. He rose and took Asher's hand. "Son," he said as the lines in his swarthy face seemed to soften, "do you know a wench named Deborah?"

Asher's face brightened for a moment. "Yes," he said. "But why do you ask?"

"She came here, shaking with fright, but bringing you some food. Unfortunately it's against the rules for prisoners to receive gifts. But she said as she left, 'Please tell him I think he's brave.'"

"I always try to be, sir," Asher said.

"You'll have a chance to prove it," the centurion said. "There are two kinds of courage, son. One is the soldier's. That's the brand I deal in. But there's another brand. The courage of faith. I'm only beginning to understand what this second kind means." He swung open the door and beckoned to the soldiers. "This is the man who goes to Tiberias," he said. "Take him away."

6. AUDIENCE WITH HEROD

THE JORDAN, as Andrew had once remarked to Asher, was John's river.

It was a strange river, Asher knew, one of the strangest on earth. Though its source is found high among the clouds of Mount Hermon, its bed sinks deeper below sea level than that of any other river in the world.

"It is John's river," Andrew had said. "But it is the symbol of man's life."

Like man, the river Jordan begins life in innocence. Fed by the stainless snows of Mount Hermon, the Jordan at its source is a pure and crystal stream. Its waters are still unsullied by the world through which it must wind its way. But the descent is rapid—Jordan itself means "The Descender"—for the earth drags it down. Before it has reached manhood, before it has grown from stream to river, its bed has begun sinking below the level of the sea. Yet somehow it seems to struggle against its fate. It seems to struggle against the deep attraction of the earth, to delay, at least, its inevitable fate. After passing through the Sea of Galilee it continues in its tortured and snakelike course, swinging now to the east, now to the west, in such a meandering way that though its grave in the Dead Sea lies only sixty-five miles to the south, it covers two hundred lingering miles to reach it.

Meanwhile, as it flows, its bed sinks deeper into the earth, deeper below the level of the sea. Its waters, too, have slowly lost the purity of early youth. Like man, it has become stained with the mud and clay of its mother earth. And when at last it pours into the lifeless waters of the Dead Sea, it is deep below sea level—twelve hundred feet below it. Its sluggish waters are almost lifeless, too—gray, brackish, clouded with all the corruption of the world.

During the early months of the year while the river was at its flood and the days were cool, John had continued preaching along the Jordan's banks near Bethabara. All mankind had come to him at this crossroads of the world—soldiers and publicans, harlots and beggars, the rich and the poor. John refused baptism in his river to no one. For, though he had made it his, he shared it with all humankind.

With the coming of summer John moved farther north where the heat was less intense and the evenings were cool. Living in the hills to the east of the Jordan, he continued preaching and baptizing for all who came to him with humble hearts.

Then early one morning there came to him a stranger from Galilee.

John, standing among his disciples in the cool of the morning, saw the stranger in white robes coming along the path toward them. Even at a distance he felt that somewhere deep in his own past he had encountered the man before. With his eyes still on the stranger, he touched the arm of one of the disciples.

"Who is this man in white robes that comes toward us?" he asked.

John's disciples looked toward the stranger. He seemed to be a man in his early thirties, a man of medium height with a short beard. He was handsome, with a radiant face. The sun, which had just risen above the eastern hills, shone now full upon his features so that they seemed to glow with all the golden light of dawn.

"We do not know him, Master," Andrew said.

His eye still fastened on the approaching figure, John waited in silence. Somewhere beneath his rough coat of camel's hair he felt a strange stirring of excitement and expectation as if around or beneath his heart something—a thought, a word, a dream remembered—had suddenly become alive. He stood there wondering . . .

Only a few years before he had asked a question of his mother, Elisabeth, as she lay dying. She had sent word to him in the wilderness, asking him to come to her. John's father, Zacharias, had been dead for many years and she was alone.

Holding her son's hand as he sat at her bedside, she had murmured to him the strange story of his birth. John had already heard parts of it. His father himself had told him how the Angel Gabriel had suddenly appeared in the temple in Jerusalem while Zacharias was performing his priestly duties there. Gabriel had told Zacharias that his wife, Elisabeth, was to bear him a son whose name was to be John. This son was to prepare the way for the coming Messiah. He would go before the Messiah in the spirit and power of Elijah and make ready a people prepared for the Lord.

As Elisabeth lay dying, she told her son the rest of the story, which she had all the years kept secret. She spoke with difficulty and her mind wandered a little, but her eyes were still a clear dark blue like his own.

"Six months," she began, "six months after your father had seen this vision in the temple, my cousin Mary came here to me. She brought a strange and wonderful story."

John waited as his mother paused, struggling for breath. "Speak in a whisper if it's easier for you," he said. "What story had she come to tell?"

Elisabeth lay for a long time without answering. Then, as if waking from a dream, she smiled into her son's face. "I met Mary at the door," she resumed. "It had been a long time since I had seen her and I didn't expect her then. Six months had passed since I had learned I was to bear you, my son. I had told no one, and yet Mary knew. And I knew, too, what news she had come the long way to tell me. For as we embraced each other I felt a deep stirring of recognition, John, beneath my heart."

She smiled again into her son's eyes.

"But what was the news, Mother, that Mary brought you?" John asked as he bent down more closely to her face, for her voice was growing weaker and the light was fading. "What did she tell you? What was it that you recognized?"

Haltingly, in broken sentences, Elisabeth then told him Mary's story: how one evening the Angel Gabriel had appeared suddenly in her room and in a blaze of light had told Mary that she was to bring forth a son whose name was to be Jesus, the Son of God. When Mary had asked Gabriel how this could be, the angel had told her that the power of the Highest would over-shadow her and the Holy Ghost would come upon her, for, he had said, "with God nothing shall be impossible."

"She brought me this story," Elisabeth whispered. "She came all the way to this hill country to tell me."

"And you have kept this secretly in your heart, Mother? All these years?"

She answered only with a gentle smile.

"But, Mother," John said as his hand grew firmer on her own. "Tell me, Mother. How am I to know the Messiah when I meet him? How am I to recognize my Lord?"

Elisabeth opened her eyes and looked into her son's face, her eyes wandering dimly over his mouth, his hair, his forehead, in a last lingering regard.

"Tell me, Mother," John repeated. "How am I to know him when we meet?"

His mother smiled into his face. "You already have recognized him," she said. "You will know him truly when you meet again."

Such were his mother's last words to him. And now, as the stranger in white garments came toward him, John remembered. As the distance between the two men narrowed, recognition swept through him in a sudden flood, and he knew that the man walking toward him through the cool air of morning was the Messiah.

Gesturing to the disciples to remain behind, he started down the path toward Jesus.

The two met in silence for they had both recognized each other, and there was no need for greeting.

"I have come to you," Jesus said simply. "I have need to be baptized."

John was startled by the request. "Nay!" he protested. "I have need to be baptized of thee, and comest thou to me?"

Jesus laid his hand on John's shoulder. "Let it be so now," he said. "It is fitting for thee to baptize me in order to fulfill all righteousness."

But John was still troubled. Since his youth he had awaited this coming of the Messiah, he had worked to prepare the way for this Son of God, the laces of whose sandals, he often said, he wasn't worthy to unbind. And yet now this sinless man, like any one of the hundreds who had come to him, was humbly asking for John's baptism of repentance. What was he to do?

Walking side by side, the two remained deep in converse while John's disciples, gathered on a hill nearby, watched in silent awe.

At noon the disciples saw the two descend together to the Jordan and with straining eyes watched as their master baptized the Messiah.

Beholding the scene from their vantage point above the river, the river that John at this moment shared with all humanity, the disciples became aware, dimly at first, but with ever deepening emotion, that this act they were witnessing from afar was the supreme moment of John's life. The moment had come swiftly, unexpectedly. For John's disciples well knew that though their master had prepared the way for the Messiah, had been his forerunner and herald, he had in his deep humility never imagined that the Messiah he longed so greatly to see would, in all humility, too, ask to be baptized by John. Though it gave the Messiah's sanction to the ministry of his forerunner, a few of them were aware, vaguely perhaps, but with sorrow, that this act might mark the climax and end of John's career. But even though it was the supreme act of John's life, he administered the baptism swiftly and simply, as if the Messiah were the humblest of mortals.

The baptism done, Jesus went up straightway from the water and disappeared among the hills, while John returned to his disciples, his dark blue eyes aglow with all the reflected radiance of the sun. But he seemed beyond words and said nothing to them.

Not until the following day did John speak. As he watched Jesus walking and meditating by himself, John, turning to Andrew and another disciple who were standing by, said with a gesture of his hand, "Behold the Lamb of God!"

There was something in the manner in which John spoke the words, something in the expression of his face and the gesture of his hand, that made Andrew realize that John was notifying them that his task was done. True, the people might still flock around him and clamor for baptism. But it was his duty now only to make plain to them that the Messiah had come. John had fulfilled his mission, and Andrew was at liberty to follow the new master whom the Baptist now designated with a gesture of his hand.

Torn by sorrow at leaving John, but eager to follow the Messiah, Andrew and another disciple hastened away. And, catching up with Jesus where he walked, they joined him and spent the remainder of the day listening to his teachings. It was the turning point in both their lives.

On the following day, bidding the Baptist farewell, Andrew gathered up his belongings and left for Galilee to bring tidings of the Messiah to his brother Simon, a fisherman of Capernaum.

Upon reaching Tiberias, the great new city Herod Antipas had built on the western shores of the Sea of Galilee, Asher had once again been locked in prison. But not for long this time. A few evenings after his ar-

rival in Tiberias, as twilight glimmered beyond the
window, he heard the tramp of feet coming toward his
cell. A key turned in the lock, the door opened, and
Asher, springing to his feet, found himself staring at a
man whose face he recognized. It was the lean, un-
pleasant face of the official who had questioned him so
sharply when he was first arrested.

"Are you prepared to tell your story?" the official
asked.

"I have been ready for a long time," Asher said.

The official studied Asher with obvious disgust. "But
you're a mass of filthy rags!" He turned to the jailer
who stood behind him. "Have him taken to the palace
baths. I'll have clothes sent to him there. And tell them
to hold him until I come."

Then, turning on his heel, he left.

Escorted by two soldiers, Asher was led to the baths
connected with the great palace. There, in a great
steaming room, a half-dozen slaves, under the cold eyes
of an officer, washed and scrubbed him, smeared his
hair with fragrant ointment, and dressed him in a robe
so soft and delicate that Asher felt he was being trans-
formed into a girl.

Washed, combed, and dressed—his own filthy clothes
were wrapped in a bundle and hastily spirited away—
Asher was taken by the official into the palace. After
passing through a series of marble corridors, they entered a room whose walls were decorated with the
painted figures of strange men with horns and hairy
legs like goats. Asher stood staring, awe-stricken by

the pictures and the gilded furniture. He waited for instructions.

The official, who had seated himself in one of the chairs, finally looked up from a letter he was reading.

"You're about to be led into Herod's presence," he said. "Be prepared to answer his questions briefly. Address him as 'Sire,' but above all, make your story short. The tetrarch is easily bored, as you may discover."

"I'll try to be brief," Asher agreed. "But should I tell him *all* my story?"

"Why not?" the official asked.

"I mean," Asher began, then stopped, for he had become frightened suddenly at what might happen to him if he told the whole truth. "I mean, should I tell the tetrarch that it was his wife, Herodias, who hired the killers?"

"What do you suppose you're here for?" the official said. "Did not the centurion explain?"

"He told me that no one else dared to tell the truth to Herod," Asher said.

"Was that all he said?"

Asher remained silent. He wasn't sure if he could trust the official. Should he tell him the centurion thought that Asher's story might possibly save John's life? "He told me to tell the truth," Asher said finally.

"Did he also inform you that to tell the truth might be dangerous?"

"Yes," Asher said.

"Your friend the Baptist has spoken disagreeable

truths," the official observed. "Are you afraid to speak them?"

"No," Asher said.

"Speak up, then," the official said. "And if you're like John, you'll ask for no reward." He smiled cynically. "And get none."

The door opened. A page in a brown silk robe entered and stepped up to the official.

"The tetrarch is ready," he announced.

The official rose. "In a good temper?" he asked.

The page shrugged his shoulders. "While I answered that question his temper might turn sour," he said. "I advise you to waste no time."

The official gestured to Asher to follow, and the three entered a large, dark room. Its walls were hung with the horns of wild animals and with hunting weapons— spears, bows, javelins. At one end, before a squat table —dressed in all the barbaric splendor the Herods affected—sat Herod Antipas. He was toying idly with the shaft of an arrow tipped with a scarlet feather. He was a man of about fifty, with a sharp, pointed beard, a dark face, and black eyes that seemed constantly in motion.

When the page had bowed and withdrawn from the room, Herod motioned for the two to come closer. He studied Asher for several moments. "Is this fop here your simple shepherd boy?" he asked suspiciously.

The official grinned. "He was in foul rags when I found him, Sire," he said. "I had him scrubbed and garbed decently for the audience with your highness."

"Well done!" said Herod. He kept his eyes on Asher. "Are you a liar?" he asked suddenly.

Taken aback by the question, Asher could at first only shake his head. "I try not to be, Sire," he managed to stammer.

Herod nodded. "They tell me that you have a story to tell about a pair of assassins hired to kill my good friend, John the Dipper. I also understand that you were suspected of having stabbed one of them. Tell your story from the beginning."

Abashed, fumbling for words, Asher began. He told how he had seen the two men dressed as Essenes come along the road, how he had observed the dagger beneath the robe of one of them, and how he had crawled up to the fire where they were broiling their meat and had overheard their conversation.

Herod, glancing occasionally at the official as if seeking his assurance that Asher was telling the truth, listened without obvious boredom. Asher reached the point of telling how the older of the two men had warned his younger confederate that their murderous plot must at all costs be kept secret from the king. Herod leaned forward in his chair. His eyes narrowed.

"It was to be kept secret from me?" he asked, his black eyes burning with anger and suspicion. "Did he say why?"

"Yes," said Asher. "He did."

"Speak up!" Herod exclaimed. "Why were they at all costs to keep it secret from Herod?"

"Because," Asher said, "the person who had hired them feared to be made known to you."

"And who was this person who dared hire them to do this thing?"

Asher glanced toward the official, but he seemed to have become absorbed in a study of his sleeve. Asher thought he detected a faint smile on his narrow mouth. "It was Herodias, your wife, who had hired them," Asher said.

Herod started at the name. Quickly composing himself, but with his black eyes blazing, he turned on the official. "Why was I not told this before?" he demanded.

"If it please your highness," the official said, "I was not certain of my territory. My duties, I feared, did not extend into the royal bedchamber."

Herod plucked angrily at his sharp beard. "Was anyone else a party to this conspiracy?"

"We have learned, Sire," the official said in a silky voice, "that the chamberlain engaged these assassins, and in the presence of your honorable wife."

"Put the chamberlain to torture!" Herod burst out, but a moment later he thought better of it. "No. I shall take care of him myself. Or should I?" He was silent for a moment. "But didn't this assassin confess anything besides the murder of his accomplice? He did not confess the plot?"

"No," the official said, smiling. "He dared confess nothing but murder."

"Why?" asked Herod.

"He feared the chamberlain, he feared your highness,

but most of all he feared . . ." The official paused as if searching for a word.

"My wife," Herod finished the sentence. "Yes, there are many who fear her. But under further pressure could not this assassin be made to sing?"

"No longer—his tongue is silent," the official said. "He is dead."

"Dead? And how is that?"

"Alas, while the poor fellow was meditating in his lonely cell, a lady of your acquaintance sent him a basket of poisoned figs."

Herod's face darkened. "What murderous flowers spring from a woman's hate!" he muttered. For a long while he remained silent as he studied the tip of the arrow he held. Then, gesturing to Asher with the shaft, he bade him come closer. "Shepherd," he said, "have you been dipped by this Baptizer?"

"Not yet," Asher confessed. "But I mean to be."

"They say he's Elijah come back to life. Have you seen him close?"

"I have talked with him."

Herod leaned forward. "Tell me, lad," he whispered. "Does he cast a shadow?"

Puzzled by the strange question, Asher stood silent.

"If he casts no shadow, then he is a ghost, a spirit," Herod said. "Speak up, you fool! Did you see his shadow?"

"I believe I did, Sire," Asher stammered.

"He is no ghost, then. No Elijah. Doubtless he has a demon, a devil, who speaks through his mouth and

teaches him wonders. It is because of this demon that
people do what he bids them. When he bids them fast,
they fast. When he bids them pray, they pray. If he
should say to them: 'Rise up, children of Israel, against
Herod,' they would rise up and overwhelm me. Should
I have John slain, or should some other slay him, the
demon would find another and more dangerous mouth
to speak through. Yes, I must protect him. I must keep
John safe."

All through this long speech—which Herod seemed
to be making to himself rather than to any audience—
the official stood nodding gravely, though the sardonic
smile still played around the corners of his mouth. Finally, when Herod had ceased speaking, the official
cleared his throat.

"As your highness knows, this John has a powerful
enemy at court. It will be most difficult to protect the
prophet from the wiles of such an enemy."

Herod sat in silence for several moments, biting his
heavy lips and staring at the official. Finally, his mouth
narrowed to a crafty, foxlike smile.

"There is a method of protecting him," he said, "from
every danger. We will place him out of harm's way."
He paused.

"I await your command," the official said.

"Arrest him," Herod said. "Place this prophet in protective custody in the dungeon at Machaerus. He will
be safe there."

"A brilliant solution!" exclaimed the official. "I will

give orders for his arrest. And this young shepherd—is he to be imprisoned, too?"

"Are there any charges against him?" Herod asked.

"None," said the official. "Unless he has lied to us."

"He has proved himself an honest and straightforward witness," Herod said. "Is he in danger, too?"

"Yes. If he returns to the Baptist. He will be safe if he remains hidden."

"Release him," Herod said. "As for the chamberlain, arrest him secretly. I cannot safely question him myself. Perhaps he might sing for you, however, in one of your little music chambers."

The official smiled. "They are always at your highness's service," he said with a bow.

The tetrarch nodded and then raised his hand to notify them that the audience had ended. Side by side, Asher and the official bowed themselves out of the room.

7. IN THE DUNGEON OF MACHAERUS

RELEASED THE NEXT MORNING from further imprisonment by Herod's order, Asher left Tiberias and set forth for Nain, where he hoped to find Deborah and her father. They could tell him, he thought, where Andrew and the Baptist were. Though he knew that there was danger for him if he were seen in the company of John's disciples, he nevertheless was determined to bring them warning that the Baptist was in peril of immediate arrest.

The official had turned Asher loose at the palace gate. He was still dressed in the luxurious robes he had worn before Herod. He felt uncomfortable in them, but he realized they might help to conceal his identity, in case Herodias had sent her spies to track him down.

It was a long day's journey from Tiberias to Nain. The gaily colored anemones Deborah had described were no longer in bloom, but Mount Tabor with its dome-shaped crest rose to the south, while far behind him towered snow-capped Mount Hermon.

91

It was twilight when Asher reached the walls of
Nain. A funeral procession was winding through the
gates as he entered. Inquiring his way from a merchant
who was closing up his shop, Asher found Deborah's
home without difficulty. It was Deborah herself who
answered his knock. But in all his finery she did not
recognize him at first. It was only when he began
speaking that she knew. Laughing with surprise and
delight at his fine clothes, she called all her family to
see who had arrived.

"I've been worried sick about you," she confided.
"Your friend Andrew told us that you'd been taken to
Tiberias. We all were afraid that something dreadful
had happened."

"Where's Andrew now?" Asher asked.

"He's with his brother Simon," Deborah said. She
gazed at Asher with her melting eyes. "Will you ever
forgive me for getting you into all this trouble?"

Asher squeezed her hand. "It gave me a chance to
serve the Baptist," he said.

Zaccheus and his wife came into the room. The old
man greeted Asher like a lost son, but Asher cut the
greetings short.

"The Baptist is in danger," he said. "Herod has ordered his arrest. Where can I find him?"

"Somewhere beyond Jordan," Zaccheus said. "But
many of his disciples have left him. They say they have
found the Messiah, a man from Nazareth named Jesus."

"The Messiah has come!" Asher exclaimed. "And does
John know?"

"He has already baptized him," Zaccheus said. "Andrew left and followed him. He and another, the one called John, have become disciples of this man Jesus."

"Have you seen him?"

"Not yet, but we know some of his family. They say that he is healing the sick and performing miracles. Let me tell you of one . . ."

Deborah and her mother meanwhile had scurried around bringing in food. The family gathered around and watched happily while Asher ate the figs and bread and cheese they brought him. Asher listened to the stories about the Messiah. Then he told them of his audience with Herod.

"I must hasten tomorrow to warn John that he is in danger of arrest," Asher said. "I must warn him to flee."

"He should cross the Jordan into Judea, into Pilate's domains," Zaccheus remarked. "But do you know where to find the Baptist?"

"No," Asher admitted.

"I will go with you, my son," Zaccheus said. "I know all the roads well. We will search for the Baptist together."

Asher gratefully accepted the offer.

Later that evening, when they were alone for a moment, Deborah touched Asher's sleeve. "Asher," she said, "are you leaving me again?"

"I have a job to do," he replied. "I can't rest until I've done it."

"But you'll come back to me?"

Asher looked into her eyes. "Yes," he said. "But not

before I've proved to myself that I'm someone worthy of love."

"You're beginning to frighten me," Deborah murmured. "But I like you all the better for it."

"It's partly your doing," Asher said as he took her hand. "Perhaps if you hadn't come along that evening I'd still be tending my sheep and trying to forget that I had betrayed the Baptist."

"But you'll come back to me?"

"Yes," Asher said. "I'll come back to you. No matter what happens."

At dawn the next morning Zaccheus and Asher set out at a rapid pace for the Jordan valley. As Zaccheus knew the roads well, they made good time. Crossing the Jordan at Bethshean, they encountered some pilgrims, who told them that John had been baptizing during the summer at the springs in Enon near to Salim on the western side of the river. However, he had recently recrossed the Jordan and moved south with his disciples toward the river Jabbok.

Quickening their pace, Asher and Zaccheus made their way along the east bank of the Jordan. As they walked, Zaccheus told him more about Andrew.

"He came to us," Zaccheus said, "a day or so after we had all been baptized. He was bursting with excitement, for he had met this Jesus, a Galilean like ourselves. He said that he was on his way to fetch his brother Simon."

"Are they abandoning the Baptist?" Asher asked.

"It can't be called that," Zaccheus explained. "The Baptist is fearless, stubborn, strong, but his greatest virtue is humility. When he found the Messiah and baptized him, he knew that his work was done and that his disciples should turn to the Messiah. Some men, even great ones like John, have to be second in God's plan."

"He's a brave man," Asher said.

"He is like the ford at Bethabara where he began his preaching," Zaccheus said. "A ford through which we children of Israel must pass from Moses to the Messiah. But it takes courage for a preacher of John's power and influence to relinquish his position willingly—nay —gladly."

Asher thought a moment. "Do you think, now that John's disciples are leaving him for Jesus, Herod will be less afraid of him? That Herodias herself may be less vengeful?"

Zaccheus shook his head. "Herod perhaps may prove more lenient—Herodias never. She will never forgive him for publicly denouncing her divorce and sinful marriage to Antipas. Her heart smolders with revenge."

"What enemies surround him!" Asher exclaimed in despair. "Herod would silence him by arrest. Herodias would silence him forever with the sword. Perhaps they have already seized him."

"We must make haste," Zaccheus said.

That night they slept along the banks of the Jordan. But early the next morning they encountered one of John's disciples, an Essene, on his way to Capernaum.

Learning of the reason for their mission, he gave them alarming news.

"You won't find him among his disciples," he said. "The Baptist has left for Tiberias."

"For Tiberias!" Asher and Zaccheus were stunned.

"Yes," the Essene replied. "Two days ago he departed." Then he explained that John, realizing for some time that he was in danger of arrest, had gone with one of his disciples to demand an audience with Herod.

"But why?" Zaccheus asked. "Has he gone to appeal for clemency? For permission to preach and baptize freely?"

"Nay, my friends. He has gone to Tiberias to denounce the corruption of the court and Herod's adulterous marriage to his brother's wife."

Zaccheus stared at the Essene in dismay. "But it's madness!"

"Madness perhaps to some, but to the Baptist it's a duty. A true prophet acts as well as preaches."

"Where are the rest of the disciples?" Asher inquired.

"Just north of the river Jabbok," the Essene explained. "Not far from the spot where it pours into the Jordan."

Asher was puzzled. Where should he go? Tiberias? But he realized that John could not escape arrest now even if he wished to. In fact, the Baptist might already be on his way to Machaerus. Asher decided that it was best for him to continue to the river Jabbok where he could consult with John's disciples and inform them that their leader was being taken to the distant fortress. He explained to Zaccheus what his plans were.

Realizing that he could be of little further help to him, Zaccheus reluctantly bade Asher farewell; leaving him to find the Jabbok alone, he set forth for Nain with the friendly Essene.

Asher continued south along the Jordan. A day and a half later he found the disciples encamped on a hill overlooking the Jabbok. They listened to his story with obvious alarm.

"The dungeons of Machaerus are the most terrible in all Palestine," one of the disciples said. "They are ovens in summer, icy pits in winter. Few men have ever come out of them alive."

"Let us pray Herod changes his mind," Asher said. "And who went with John?"

"Philip," the disciples told him. "He would take only one of us. He ordered us to wait here for a message."

"And it's indeed true that he means to demand an audience with Herod to denounce the marriage?" Asher inquired.

They said that such was his purpose. "There was no persuading him not to," one of the disciples said. "He was determined to go and to go immediately. For some time he has had forebodings that he was to be seized and he wished to make his protest to Herod while he was still a free man, a free agent. He said that his protest would lose its weight if he made it as a prisoner. But we all fear that it's the last we will see of him. We are waiting now for Philip to return with news."

Asher could hardly remove their apprehensions with
any encouraging words of his own. Taking up quarters
with the disciples, he waited impatiently for Philip's return, but it was a week before he appeared. The story
he brought filled the disciples with dismay, but their
hearts swelled with pride at the daring, the fearless
courage of their leader. They listened breathless as
Philip told the story.

John, Philip told them, had demanded an audience
as soon as he had reached Tiberias, and to the wonder
of everyone, Herod had granted it. And he had, at the
Baptist's insistence, agreed to even more. He had agreed
to bring Herodias to the audience with him.

"It was held in the palace courtyard," Philip began,
"at about the sixth hour. John and I were brought in by
the chamberlain and a squad of soldiers. The courtyard
was crowded with courtiers, army men and officials.
Herod and the queen sat on twin thrones against the
east wall with a purple tapestry behind them. John and
I were marched up to within five paces of their thrones.

"Herod stared at John. His face seemed full of curiosity. Then he turned to the chamberlain. 'Stand the
Baptizer in the sun,' said he. 'Let me see his shadow, if
he can cast one.' The chamberlain moved John a few
paces back into the noon sun. Herod and all the courtiers craned their necks to look. For a long time Herod
studied the black shadow on the marble flags. He turned
to Herodias. 'The shepherd lad was right,' he said. 'See!
He is no ghost, no spirit. He is a man.'

"Herodias said nothing, but I watched her suck in

her crimson lips, watched her black eyes narrow with spite.

"'Speak now,' Herod then said to John. 'You have denounced us before. Let us hear again what that demon of yours has in its mind to tell us. Speak and be done with it!'

"For a long while John remained silent, standing there with folded arms as he looked into their eyes. He was a strange figure, indeed, with his leather belt and rough coat among that perfumed throng. Suddenly one of the courtiers tittered. Herod turned on him in fury. 'Fling that fop out!' he screamed. Then he stared at John. 'In the name of all the gods I bid you speak!'

"The Baptist raised his arm above his head. His fist was clenched. He looked first at Herod and then at Herodias. I know him well. Many times have I watched him preach, but never yet have I seen such wrath in his eyes."

Philip paused a moment and looked around him. "I quailed at the very sight of him. Then he spoke and it was like Malachi. 'Ye brood of vipers,' he began. 'Ye Herods! Behold the day cometh, it burns like a furnace. And all ye proud and all ye that live wickedly shall be like stubble. The day approaches when fire will leave ye neither root nor branch.'

"I saw Herod's face blanch at the words, but Herodias sat frozen with blazing eyes, twisting a sapphire ring round and round her little finger. There was a contemptuous smile on her lips. I feared for the Baptist, for the crowd around us had begun to murmur, but he continued while the courtyard echoed with his thundering voice. He denounced the morals of the court, he denounced the marriage and called both Herod and Herodias the wreckers of two homes. He spoke of Salome, Herodias' only daughter, and he charged the queen with estranging the girl from her own father. 'The sins are visited upon the children,' he said. 'May God protect the girl.' His condemnation was complete, fearless. Herod sat there silent beside his wife, his face now black with rage, now white with terror. Finally the Baptist ended. 'I have done,' he said. 'I have spoken.' Thus the audience before the king ended."

Philip paused and looked around him. "They have taken him to Machaerus," he said.

"Will Herod put him to death there?" one of the disciples asked.

"Nay," said Philip. "Herod is a strange man, a strange ruler. In spite of the Baptist's denunciation, in spite of his wife's fury, Herod even on the next day came to visit John in the cell where they held us prisoners. He seems to hold John in awe, he becomes perplexed and overwrought when he listens to him, yet for all that he listens to him gladly and asks advice."

"Then Herod will keep him safe?" one of the disciples asked.

"From Herodias? He may try to. He is at least placing the whole length of his dominions between Herodias and John."

"Let us pray that she gets no closer," a disciple said. "But now what are we to do?"

"We must hasten to Machaerus," Philip said. "John has perhaps already arrived there."

Several days later, Asher with eight of the Baptist's disciples, skirting the shores of the Dead Sea, came in sight of the grim fortress-castle of Machaerus. Its gray towers loomed against a cloudless sky where Herod, called "the Great," had built it, high on the lofty mountain of Makhwar. As the disciples gazed upward at the walls and battlements, they cherished little hope of ever seeing their leader again. Yet a surprise awaited them.

Though Herod had ordered John lodged in a dungeon like a common criminal, he feared to deny him to his followers. Soon after they had arrived at the foot of the mountain and had forlornly pitched their tents, a messenger came from the centurion in charge of the fortress. He informed them that Herod had granted them permission to visit their master.

Joyfully, with Asher in their company, they ascended the long winding road to the castle gates and were escorted through the courtyard. Led by the jailer, they climbed down the stone stairway to the dark and sultry dungeon where John was held. Through a tiny slit in the masonry a ray of light feebly penetrated into the darkness of the crypt. Gazing down into the opening through which the Baptist had been lowered, they could vaguely make out his broad shoulders and his luminous hair. Brokenly they called down greetings to him, words of encouragement and hurried questions, for they had been warned that their visit must be brief.

John called up his answers cheerfully out of the dark pit where he stood, manacled and chained—sending his greetings to absent disciples, telling them all to have courage.

"Bring me word of the Messiah," he asked, his strong voice ringing with a hollow sound from the dungeon. "Bring me word where he is and about his preaching."

They answered that they would and tried to make their voices seem as cheerful as his own. But they were sunk in grief, and when the guard roughly told them their time was up, they climbed the stairs to the outer air with heavy hearts.

The clear, blue sky seemed cruel to Asher as he came out into it, and the Dead Sea, shimmering like molten lead below the castle, was hostile and malign. Led by the guard, they straggled across the great courtyard toward the gate. The gate swung open on its growling hinges, and Asher was about to follow the disciples when he felt a hand touch his shoulder. He whirled around. A soldier stood there.

"Follow me," he said. "The captain wants you."

Asher, startled, glanced quickly at the disciples and then, with deep forebodings, followed the soldier toward an archway, through a long corridor, and into a small room in which a large number of Roman standards were stacked in one corner. Leaving Asher there alone, the soldier closed the door behind him.

For a while Asher stood staring around him, wondering nervously what was now in store for him. He had not long to wait. The door swung open and there strode in the centurion whom he had last seen in Bethabara when he was first arrested.

"I saw you come up here," the centurion said abruptly. "Do you remember me?"

"Yes," Asher said. "You're Cornelius, the centurion."

"You can be of service to me." The centurion paused. "And to the Baptizer."

Asher was too surprised to answer.

The centurion then explained—haltingly, for he always spoke Aramaic with some difficulty—that Asher was to stay there with him ostensibly as his body servant, but that his real duty was to make the Baptist's life less miserable and to watch secretly for any attempts that might be made upon John's life.

"I will see you have the run of the palace," the centurion said. "My word is law here, except when Herod comes on his annual visit. Can I trust you with the task?"

Asher, trusting the centurion's good faith, quickly accepted. That very evening, alone and unchallenged by the guard, he went to John's dungeon and, calling down his name, lowered him the gourd full of goat's milk the centurion had sent.

Happy to be of service to the Baptist, Asher watched over him and brought him the food he asked for and even managed to bring him a scroll to read and a small lamp to light his dark crypt. When his disciples came to see John, Asher went with them. This was the most difficult of all tasks, for though John remained stout-hearted, even cheerful, under his sufferings, the disciples themselves were more woebegone each time Asher met them at the gate.

Unlike Andrew and the others who had left the Baptist to follow the Messiah, the remaining disciples seemed filled with doubts and misgivings—not about John to whom they still were loyal, but about the divine mission of Jesus.

Whether the activities of Jesus did not follow John's preconceived ideas about the Messiah, or whether his own disciples' doubts led them to misinterpret the Baptist's attitude, or whether John sent them merely in order that they could see Jesus themselves and be convinced: this Asher never clearly understood. He only knew that, some months after John had been imprisoned, he dispatched two of his disciples to ask a question for Jesus himself to answer: "Are you he who is to come, or shall we look for another?"

The two found Jesus, and after watching him heal the sick, make the blind see and the lame walk, they asked him their question: if he were the Messiah.

"Go and tell John," Jesus had replied, "what you have seen and heard. And tell him, too, for he will understand, that the poor are hearing good news." Then Jesus added as a gentle reproach to John's disciples: "And blessed is he who doesn't find me a stumbling block of doubt."

John seemed satisfied with the answer Jesus had sent him and understood its real meaning. But some of his disciples still remained dubious. Asher detected in their attitude toward Jesus a slight touch of resentment that Jesus should carry on his preaching so freely while their own master lay chained to silence in prison. But John remained brave and cheerful as the dark days dragged on.

Time passed with its seasons. Summer was hardest for John to bear. A raging sun blasted the castle under a cloudless sky. The stone flagging in the courtyard burned the feet. The thick walls of the castle scorched the hand. Soldiers on guard baked in pools of sweat, while John's black dungeon itself became a sweltering furnace. Sick at heart at the thought of John's sufferings, Asher lowered him gourds of cool water and felt ashamed of his own freedom, and of his own despair, too, whenever he heard the Baptist's strong voice call up cheerfully from the fetid depths below, thanking Asher for the little gifts he brought.

"Can't he be moved to some other cell?" Asher once asked the centurion. "Into a cell where he can get light and air?"

"I dare not move him," the centurion said. "Not until Herod comes."

"Will that be soon?"

"Not until the days grow cool. Herodias and her daughter Salome find it difficult to bear this heat."

The days crawled on. Several of John's disciples dropped away. Occasionally Asher detected a slight tremor in John's voice. Was the imprisonment sapping

John's spirit as well as his strength? Asher wondered.

But he was soon to learn that nothing—imprisonment, heat, starvation, the implacable hatred of Herodias—nothing could break that strong, brave, beating heart.

8. THE DEATH OF JOHN

WORD THAT HEROD, his wife, and her daughter Salome were on their way spread through the great castle of Machaerus like news of a pestilence. Hardly had the centurion received orders to make the great palace ready when servants and slaves from the royal household began arriving. Donkeys and mules, laden with skins of rare wines, bundles of spices, fruit, and fish from Galilee, perfumes and sweet-smelling unguents, plodded up the steep road to the castle.

Meanwhile the soldiers stationed there burnished their armor; slaves scrubbed the flags of the courtyard; carpets were unrolled and spread along the great marble stairs and on the palace floors. Bright-colored awnings were stretched over the terraces to give shade. An army of cooks and kitchen help arrived and fell to work polishing the kettles and preparing for the great birthday feast Herod gave each year.

Even John, deep in his dungeon cell, became aware of the activity and asked Asher the cause of it.

"Herod is expected," Asher said.

"And with his wife?"

"Yes," said Asher. "And her daughter, too."

"Woe to the child of a broken home," John said. "The sins of the parents are visited upon them."

"They say she is young and beautiful," Asher murmured.

"May God protect her youth and beauty from her mother's corruption!" John said. Then he thanked Asher for the cheese and wild honey he had brought.

A few days later, Herod and his family arrived.

They appeared at the gates, announced by a burst of trumpets that rang and re-echoed arrogantly from the walls of the castle. Rank upon rank stood the centurion's soldiers with their shields and standards. Clustering behind them, craning their necks to see the splendor, crowded the palace servants. Asher stood among them. But, though his ears rang with the trumpets and his mind whirled with the magnificence of Herod's entourage, his thoughts kept returning to the lonely man chained in his dungeon by Herod's superstitious fears and Herodias' bitter hatred.

With clanking armor and fluttering plumes, the palace guard marched by. Behind them, walking alone and with a slight limp, came Herod. His tunic was blood red; the head cloth he wore was green with a golden band. Asher watched the tetrarch as he passed, a set smile on his heavy lips, his black eyes darting here and there as if he walked through a ghostly wood at night.

Behind Herod, in a golden litter, came his wife, He-

rodias, half reclining on silk cushions, with a fan of pea-
cock feathers in her hand. Her eyes were black—like all
the Herods, for she was not only Herod's wife but his
own niece. Her face was covered with the thinnest of
veils and her eyes, Asher could plainly see, had been
lengthened in the Egyptian manner with purple crayon.
Her black hair was drawn back from her forehead, and
her face whitened, so that she looked not like a living
thing but like the whitened image of a lynx. She gazed
about her with a searching but contemptuous glance,
like a panther seeking out its prey. Watching her, Asher
wondered if she knew that John was perhaps within
hearing distance of the jangling timbrels that followed
her litter.

Behind a bright array of palace guards came the litter bearing the queen's young daughter, Salome. She
seemed to be about sixteen years old. Though she re-
sembled her mother in all her features, Asher noticed
that their expressions differed. There was something
petulant rather than contemptuous about Salome's pouting lips, while her black eyes seemed tinged with fear.
She glanced anxiously about her as if in dread of the
great palace she was about to enter.

Herod waited impatiently for the two women at the
foot of the stairs. When they had finally dismounted
from the litters, he led them, followed by a swarm of
courtiers, up the marble steps. Asher watched as they
disappeared into the palace . . .

Preparations for the celebration of Herod's birthday

now occupied the entire palace staff. Even Asher was set to polishing the centurion's armor, for Herod had ordered Cornelius to be present at the great banquet, not as a guest but as a watchful guard.

"Herod seems to believe that his wife is plotting something new," the centurion told Asher. "He's given orders that John be removed from his crypt to a secret room in one of the towers."

"Perhaps he'll be safe there," Asher said hopefully.

Cornelius smiled wryly. "Herod may be a fox, but he's no match for his vixen. I fear she'll find the Baptist, run him down." The old soldier paused a moment. "At times I feel like a shorn lamb in this tempest of palace plots and intrigue. I know only how to obey simple commands, and Herod has given me few during the past few days to protect John's life. It's true that Herod, for some strange reason, visits the prophet almost daily and listens to him, but I fear he worries now only about his feast." The old soldier smiled. "How does that old song go? 'When kings carouse, soldiers their duty do.' But it's hard for me to know what my duty is, whom to obey—my conscience or my master."

"Do you think Herodias may be hatching a plot," Asher asked, "to spring upon Herod when his guard is down during the feast?"

"In all likelihood," Cornelius said. "But we must keep our own guard up. We must watch like hawks. I have plans for you to help me. Get your best clothes ready."

Deeply disturbed by the centurion's forebodings that Herodias was busily planning some final plot to satisfy her craving for John's life, Asher half-heartedly got his fine clothes ready. It seemed like a trivial thing to do, though he hoped that the centurion had some definite plan of action.

It was evident that Herod himself, for the time being at least, had lost interest in preserving John's life. He was occupied in nothing now but making his great banquet a success. He seemed determined to make it surpass all previous ones, not only in the number of guests, but in the luxury of the food, the variety of the wines, and the magnificence of the entertainment. Even Herodias, it was rumored, was arranging a special dance to enliven the occasion. As for Herod, he wandered about the palace with his chief steward—giving orders, personally supervising the decorations in the great banquet hall, rehearsing the troupes of dancers, consulting the chief musician about the pieces to be played, and even visiting the kitchens, where he sampled the soups and sauces and tasted the rare wines that were to be served.

For days Asher had watched the musicians and entertainers filing through the gates with their instruments and their costumes. Finally the guests, attended by their slaves and servants, began arriving—all the lords and high captains and the chief men of Galilee. Asher, watching by the pillared gates, had never before seen such magnificence, such armor and such horses, such an array of costumes.

"And all this for a banquet!" the centurion exclaimed as he stood by Asher, watching a new batch of guests clatter through the courtyard. "It's like old Rome itself!"

"Will Herodias herself attend the feast?" Asher inquired.

"No women except the dancing girls are admitted to the banquet," Cornelius explained. "It's for men alone, though Herodias will attend at least in spirit. For days now she has been drilling a number of girls in a special dance with which she plans to surprise Herod."

"Aren't you relieved to learn that she's busying herself with something besides plots and poison?" Asher asked.

The centurion shrugged his shoulders. "Hate makes the mind fertile," he observed. "Hate and fear turn all things into weapons. We must watch her."

"But there have been no attempts on John's life?"

"That's what troubles me. It may mean that Herodias has laid a plot so subtle and so secret that she has no doubts of its success. I'm afraid John is in mortal danger."

"Have you warned Herod?"

Cornelius nodded.

"And can't he do something?"

Cornelius looked into Asher's eyes. "When two wills clash, which one triumphs? The weaker?"

Asher was distressed. "Could I see John?" he asked.

"Perhaps," Cornelius said. "This afternoon Herod has given permission for three of his disciples to visit the Baptist for a few moments. I will let you go with them. Be here in the courtyard when they arrive."

Asher's visit with John was all too brief. Led by the

centurion through a maze of winding corridors and stairs, Asher and the disciples found John in a tiny room in one of the castle towers. He rose from the table where he had been reading and held out both hands in greeting. His face was calm, his deep blue eyes as clear and fearless as they had ever been. He asked them about themselves and then asked what word they had from Andrew and John.

The disciples told him what they knew.

"And Jesus?" he asked.

Asher listened as they told John that Jesus was preaching daily in Galilee and performing cures that amazed everyone. "We hear that he has even raised people from the dead," one of the disciples said.

John was silent for a while. "And are the people listening to his preaching?" he asked.

"In throngs of thousands," they told him. "They flock to hear him. It is like the old days when you were preaching at Bethabara."

John smiled gently at the memory. "Those days are gone," he said. "The Messiah must now carry the staff. He must lead the world along the way that I tried with all my power to make straight for him." He paused. "He is the Son. It is for him to wax and for me to wane." Then with a gentle smile he lapsed into meditative silence.

Tearfully his disciples bade him farewell and departed.

Asher left with him. With heavy hearts, they followed the centurion down the winding stairs to the castle gate. Sorrowfully, he watched the disciples start downward to the plain.

The great feast began early in the evening and was soon in full swing. Asher, dressed in his fine clothes as the centurion had ordered, wandered out into the courtyard. He could hear the muffled sounds of revelry—the laughter, the shouts, the liquid sound of harp and psaltery, the clashing cymbals. High on the castle turrets, torches flared angrily against a stormy sky.

Disturbed to his depths, Asher lingered in the courtyard. He felt like being alone—almost like running away. But he knew that the centurion had work for him to do.

As the music rose and fell, as laughter and shouting filled the night, Asher wondered if John in his lonely tower—forgotten by everyone except Herodias—could hear the wild echoes of the feast.

Suddenly he heard a voice call his name. Answering, he found that Cornelius had sent a soldier to look for him.

"Where have you been?" the soldier asked in ill temper. "The centurion has been looking for you."

Asher followed the soldier into the palace, where he found Cornelius talking to a group of officers outside one of the doors of the banquet hall.

Cornelius' face was grave as he came over to Asher. "Something's in the wind," he said. "A slight matter, perhaps, but for the first time since she's been here

Herodias was seen to smile. I fear for the Baptist's life."

"What can we do?" Asher inquired.

"Follow me," the centurion said.

From within the banquet hall, a roar of applause, greeting the finale of a dance, echoed and re-echoed through the corridor as Cornelius hurried Asher toward a flight of stairs. He took Asher's arm. His orders were brief.

"I'm leaving you on a balcony overlooking the banquet hall. You'll find there among the spectators two of Herodias' ladies-in-waiting. She has placed them there to report the proceedings to her. They are dressed in black. Try to overhear what they say to each other."

"That is all?" Asher asked.

"Come to me at once if you hear anything of importance. I will be at the door where you found me just now."

He swung open a small door, and pushing Asher through it, he turned away. Asher climbed up a flight of stairs and found himself on a narrow balcony partly concealed by draperies but giving a clear view of the banquet hall. A group of women, luxuriously dressed, stood on the balcony watching the proceedings below. Noticing two women in black standing a little apart, Asher pushed his way to the rail and stood beside them.

Below him he could see the banquet. He had often tried to imagine what a feast was like, and now the whole spectacle lay before his eyes. Sprawled and lounging on couches ranged along three walls of the huge hall were the guests, more than a hundred in

number. Low tables before each couch bore plates of
food and tall beakers of wine. Servants and slaves, bearing huge platters, went from table to table serving the
guests, while others filled the wine cups from long-
necked pitchers. In the hollow square formed by the
couches, a score or more of girls dressed like nymphs
and satyrs were dancing to the sound of flutes and
timbrels.

Immediately below Asher was Herod's divan. It was
slightly raised above the others, placed in a position of
importance at the end of the hall. Two Negro soldiers,
with bright green plumes in their helmets, stood with
folded arms behind him, while the tetrarch, clad in
royal purple, reclined with a golden cup in his hand. As
he looked down upon Herod, Asher could see the lights
of the torches, flaming in sconces against the wall, reflected in the dark red wine in his cup.

Odors of food, of perfume, spices, wine, rose to
Asher's nostrils. His ears rang with the music and the
hubbub of drunken voices and the shouting. So loud
was the uproar that, though he listened attentively, he
could not make out what the two women beside him
were saying to each other. Asher waited. Suddenly,
with a crash of cymbals, the sounds ceased.

The nymphs and satyrs scampered off in a tumult of
laughter. Then the brassy throats of the trumpets
sounded a fanfare, and slowly the great bronze door
at one end of the hall swung open. As the flutes
shrilled and the timbrels thrummed and jangled in
pent-up fury, a crowd of girls dressed as various beasts

swarmed in. Freezing in dramatic postures, they stood gazing toward the door.

Another fanfare of trumpets, this time on a higher key, shook the banquet hall. Then, to the slow beat of the timbrels and the wail of flutes there came through the door a young girl, her fair young body sheathed in a leopard's skin. Only the lower part of her face was visible, for her eyes and forehead were covered with a grotesque mask crowned by a mass of writhing serpents in green and gold.

"There she comes!" Asher heard one of the women in black beside him exclaim.

"But what a mask to wear!" said the other. "Is it Medusa?"

"We will see," said the first.

Slowly, rhythmically, on slender legs the girl advanced. Reaching the space immediately before Herod's couch, she made a slight obeisance, and then, while the flutes and sackbuts moaned and the attendant dancers followed her rhythm with set postures, the girl began a slow and languorous dance.

"It's the Cyprian snake dance!" one of the women exclaimed. "Herod's always been mad about it. How clever of her mother!"

"Yes," said the other with a low laugh. "Look at him!"

Following the women's eyes, Asher gazed down at Herod. The tetrarch had raised himself up to a sitting position and now leaned forward, staring at the young dancer, his eyes fixed with fascination. In his hand he clutched his golden cup of wine, forgotten as he stared at the sinuous movements of the masked dancer before him.

Asher heard the two women beside him laugh softly.

"Look how she holds him!" one of them murmured. "He's all eyes."

"He doesn't know the price he'll pay for it," the other murmured.

"Does the girl know?"

"Not yet. Her mother was afraid to tell her. Salome's headstrong, too, like all the Herods."

At these words, Asher gripped the rail in front of him. So the dancer who held Herod fascinated was his own stepdaughter Salome! But did Herod know this? And what was the price he'd pay? Asher stared at the dancer, fascinated as Herod himself. But now he recognized Salome's petulant, half-open lips.

The two women began chattering again, but it was impossible to hear them. The music had risen slowly to a crescendo and the attendant dancers, coming to life out of their stiff posturing, had begun to dance wildly. The flutes and sackbuts moaned in mock desolation, the timbrels beat with a firmer cadence, while the drunken murmur of men's voices rose like a storm. Herod sat spellbound, like a man watching a burning city.

Finally, as it had begun, the dance ended with a clash of cymbals. The girl, flinging off her mask in a disdainful gesture, kneeled before Herod, her head bowed, her white arms outstretched. Then, springing to her feet, she raced like a frightened deer toward the door.

Herod rose unsteadily to his feet. "Salome!" he

shouted. Then: "Bring the girl back! And by all that's holy I'll give her anything she asks for, even to a half of my kingdom. Go get her for me, Petronius!"

Petronius, one of Herod's favorite captains, clambered from his couch and lurched toward the door. He returned in a few moments.

"She's consulting her mother," Asher heard the officer inform the tetrarch.

Herod frowned and, taking a sip of wine, glowered at the door through which Salome had disappeared. His face brightened as he saw her return and come across the floor toward him. Asher noted at once that all her dancer's poise, her grace, her charm, were gone. With the hideous mask dangling from her hand, her hair tangled, her eyes frightened, she came across the banquet hall toward her stepfather. Still panting, she stood for a moment before him. She murmured something.

"Speak up, girl!" Herod said with a vapid smile. "Any gift is yours for the asking, even up to half of my kingdom."

Beside him, Asher heard one of the woman laugh. "How generous he is! He's giving away half a kingdom he doesn't own."

"Hush!" said the other. "Let's hear what she asks for."

Salome had again murmured something. Herod turned to Petronius who stood near him. "What does the girl say?" he asked.

"O king, live forever!" said Petronius in a loud voice in which there seemed to be a note of sarcasm. He grinned. "The gift Salome asks for, O mighty ruler, is the head of John the Baptist on a platter!"

Someone laughed. Asher, in the dead silence that followed, saw Herod's face go white. Horrified, incapable of motion, Asher watched Herod bite savagely at his lip. He saw him fling his gold cup from his hand, splashing those near him with the red wine. For a moment he glared around him as if he were meeting a challenge. Then lunging forward, he struck Petronius across the face with the back of his hand. "Give her the head!" he shouted. "Give it to her on a platter, then!"

With these words he fell back on his divan and, snatching a cup of wine from a servant, drank it down in one draught.

Asher waited no longer. Beside him the women were smiling and nodding at each other. He flung himself through the door and clattered down the stairs. The corridor outside the banquet hall swarmed with people, already buzzing with the news of Salome's request.

"It's a belated wedding gift for her mother," he heard someone laugh.

"Yes, it seals their marriage."

Asher rushed past. He could find Cornelius nowhere. He ran to the barracks, but no one had seen him there. Returning to the palace, he frantically stopped everyone he met. "They're beheading the Baptist!" he told them. "Where is Cornelius, the centurion?"

People shrugged their shoulders. Some laughed at his excitement. A Negro slave rolled his eyes in terror at the news and murmured a prayer.

Asher felt trapped in a nightmare—a nightmare that did not seem to be his own, a nightmare someone else was having.

Thinking that Cornelius might be looking for him there, Asher started up the stairs to the balcony. Suddenly he heard a murmur of voices and the tramp of feet. Halfway up the stairs, he swung around.

Along the corridor, marching at the head of a small procession, came Petronius. In mock solemnity, his head bowed in an exaggerated expression of grief, he bore one of the Roman standards. Behind him tottered a pair of tipsy musicians playing a dead march on their flutes. They were followed by a squad of six soldiers.

Asher ran up a few steps to see better, for a crowd now swirled around the procession. From this vantage point he could observe that in the hollow square formed by the soldiers, there strutted a young male dancer, his leering mouth painted crimson. He had draped the Baptist's coat of camel's hair over his naked shoulders, while before him he held at arm's length a silver platter on which rested, partly concealed by a scarlet cloth, the Baptist's head.

Weak with horror, Asher could not move. He gripped the stair rail to steady himself. The macabre procession moved on. Bringing up the rear alone, marched grimly centurion Cornelius. He raised his eyes as he passed, and for a moment their glances met. The old centurion's face was set, but in his eyes Asher could read a plea for understanding, even forgiveness. "I'm an old soldier," his eyes seemed to say. "A soldier can only obey his orders."

Heartsick, his blood running like melted snow through his veins, Asher watched the standard and the dreadful procession behind it pass through the door into the banquet hall. A roar of applause and drunken laughter greeted it. The door swung shut.

Asher tarried no longer. He rushed headlong from the palace and fled across the courtyard. The storm that had threatened all evening had broken and was now venting its fury on the castle. In a black deluge of rain, Asher pushed his way through the gate. He heard a guard's muffled cry, but he plunged down the twisting mountain road ahead of him.

Far below him, livid in a flash of lightning, lay the Dead Sea—flat, impassive, leaden, like the face of death itself. Asher stumbled on. A massive clap of thunder shook the mountain to its very roots. The ground quivered beneath his feet. Asher stopped short. Had he heard a voice? For out of the thunder, echoing relentlessly from the distant hills, above the roar of wind and rain, he heard, or thought he heard, John's mighty voice crying his eternal words. "Repent ye!" the voice seemed to thunder, "Repent ye, for the kingdom of heaven is at hand!"

Suddenly, alone in the darkness, Asher felt courage, faith, hope, surge into his heart. A flood of rain crashed around him. But fortified now, filled with a new strength, he hastened on. Blackness was all about him, but blackness, he knew, was not ahead. He knew now where he was to go. John was sending him into life again. To Galilee, to Deborah, to Andrew, and to the gentle Messiah. Like a brave soldier, a soldier of the faith, Asher obeyed.

EPILOGUE

I T HAD BEEN a broad step for Asher. From a simple
shepherd lad, ignorant of the Law and the Prophets,
untutored in religion, he had developed swiftly into the
manhood of a new faith. John had made the path
straight for him, and he had gone straight from John
the Baptist to Jesus the Messiah. Others would take
the same path—the path Andrew and Simon Peter had
already taken—but centuries would elapse before many
could find the way.

But Asher had seen the Baptist. He had talked with
the Forerunner and listened to the burning message of
faith and hope that he had brought with him out of the
wilderness. John had prepared the way for Christ's
coming, and he had sacrificed his own life for that purpose. He knew that death faced him, but he had faith,
courage, and that rarest of all gifts—humility. John was
not the Light, that he well knew, but he had come to
bear witness of the Light. It was through the Baptist's

own clear eyes that the world first saw the dawn of a new faith and a new religion.

The baptism of repentance that John brought into the dark world around him was a new thing, and it will forever be new in an evil world. For though the baptism of repentance may wash away the sins of one's past, that is only a beginning. Repentance must, as John constantly repeated, bear fruit, for without fruit man is a barren tree. To reach Christ, to reach the gentle teacher of Galilee, one must make one's own road straight through the wilderness of this world. We must follow the way the Baptist has shown us—after his example, constantly speak the truth, boldly rebuke vice, and patiently suffer for the truth's sake.

ABOUT THE AUTHOR

SLATER BROWN is a writer—poet, translator, short-story writer, mystery writer, and young people's book author. Except for four years on the editorial staff of a national magazine, he has been a free-lance writer since the end of World War I, during which he served as an ambulance driver with poet E. E. Cummings. He is author of the novels, *The Burning Wheel* and *The Talking Skyscraper,* and a volume in the young people's American Heritage series, *Gray Bonnets: In the Days of Roger Williams.*